Quantum-Integral Medicine

Quantum-Integral Medicine

Towards a New Science of Healing and Human Potential

Michael Wayne, Ph.D., L.Ac.

*i*Think Books

Quantum-Integral Medicine:
Towards a New Science of Healing and Human Potential

Cover Design: Barbara Hodge
Interior Design: MyLinda Butterworth
Cover Pysanka: Sofika—www.sofika.com
Pysanka Photo: L. Zielyk

ISBN-13: 978-0-97667-970-7
ISBN-10: 0-9766797-0-1

Printed in the United States of America
10 9 8 7 6 5 4 3 2 1

Published by *i*Think Books • Saratoga Springs, NY

Contents

Acknowledgements

I have been on a personal quest for quite some time to find what I consider to be the holy grail of medicine, healing, and human potential. Without the help of certain key people, my quest would have been fruitless. First and foremost is Dr. Gail Marien. Dr. Marien served as my mentor and gave of herself time and time again as she helped me to expand my thinking and become more rounded in my concepts.

Dr. Bob Nunley also played an important part in my work, always making himself available, despite his very busy schedule, to help guide me along.

To my teachers at Pacific College of Oriental Medicine, and especially Greg Bantick, Bob Damone, Z'ev Rosenberg, and Dr. Min Fan, I am eternally indebted to you for sharing your wisdom about such a sophisticated form of medicine. My only hope is that one day Dr. Min will be able to sink a basket.

And to my patients, you have probably been my greatest teachers, as you have taken me into your confidence and allowed me to peer into the intimacies and intricacies of human nature.

My book's transformation from manuscript to book could not have been done without the keen insight and assistance of all the talented people who played a role: Charles Patterson, the book editor; MyLinda Butterworth, the interior book designer; Barbara Hodge, the cover designer; Sofia Zielyk, who graciously allowed her pysanka to adorn the cover; and Javier Perez, of Page-Turner Publicity, who has worked hard to help get my book the publicity it deserves.

Lastly, to Jacqueline and Dakota, for believing in my vision, and for continually reminding me of what the real lessons of life are.

Prologue

Each patient carries his own doctor inside him. They come to us not knowing that truth. We are at our best when we give the doctor who resides within each patient a chance to go to work.

—Albert Schweitzer

I s there an innate healing system within the body, capable of facilitating the healing process? If there is, could it be an aspect of our human potential? And if this is so, what is the mechanism that triggers this potential? For millennia, many scientists, philosophers, healers, and spiritually minded people have asked these very same questions.

These are also questions that have intrigued me for some time. As a Licensed Acupuncturist, with over 20 years experience in Chinese Medicine, my interest stems from firsthand clinical experience, having observed countless numbers of people with seemingly intractable illnesses. I have often wondered what it would take for these people to heal, and what holds them back from doing so.

There is a substantial body of evidence to support the reality of dramatic healings, and for me the evidence, both scientific and anecdotal, weighs heavily in favor of this reality. Yet, very little is known about it. Modern medicine tends to discount it, believing that these types of cases are statistical blips on the radar screen.

I am of the strong belief that we all are capable of tapping into a wellspring of healing potential and that this healing potential is an integral part of our human potential. It is well known that we use just an infinitesimal amount of our potential. The question is: can this potential be harnessed and directed at will? In this book I explore this question. My goal is to try to develop a credible theory to explain it. I have written it in such a way that I hope appeals to both the scientific and not-so-scientific-minded readers.

The first thing I explore, before anything else, is the scientific way of looking at the world—its mindset, worldview, or mental model. I felt it important to explore modern science's worldview and show how it assumes a somewhat mechanical universe, when in fact the opposite—a dynamic and nonlinear universe—is the case, as growing numbers of scientists (and philosophers and spiritual teachers) are demonstrating clearly.

In studying and surveying the rich history of medicine, science, philosophy, and spiritual traditions, I discovered that all these fields have had representatives who have eloquently and conclusively demonstrated that the universe is an open-ended one and that the laws of nature are non-linear and dynamic. Unfortunately, this information is often ignored in the name of maintaining the status quo, which subscribes to a universe that is closed and based on linear and deterministic laws. The root of the problem is that the belief of a closed universe is the prevailing scientific mental model. This mental model, like all mental models, is perpetuated by the various institutions that influence us throughout the different periods of our lives—education, religion, family, business, health care, politics, and so on.

In actuality, it is not just scientists who maintain the mental model of a closed universe. The great majority of us subscribe to the same concept, thanks to all the institutions we come into contact with throughout our lives. Therefore, I believe the first important step to cultivating greater human potential is changing this mental model most of us carry around. That is why I spend the first part of the book discussing this and why I then go on to show that the scientific evidence solidly demonstrates that ours is an open-ended universe.

At one time it was considered heresy to believe in a universe that was dynamic, infinite, and open ended: the Church burned people at the stake during the Inquisition for stating as such. Although that is a sad legacy of our past, we still attack those who don't subscribe to the accepted and prevailing dogma. Yet, as I state in Chapter 4, "dogmas are the enemy of an open-ended universe."

If you subscribe to the concept of an open-ended universe, then I believe you will ultimately have to accept that the mind and body have infinite potential. That brings me back to the primary question: how do we tap into this potential and cultivate it? I attempt to answer this question by first making the case for an open-ended universe; then, I explore the sciences that demonstrate this. Finally, I explore the worldview that expands the picture to include a universe predicated on both scientific and spiritual laws. It is from this perspective that I make the case for the medicine that I call a Quantum-Integral Medicine, a medicine that includes scientific and spiritual laws that demonstrate our universe is dynamic, infinite, and creatively evolving and emerging.

As you read this book, you will discover that Quantum-Integral Medicine is a broad field that covers a diverse range of topics—from healing and human potential, to education, creative thinking and perspective, to the new sciences, spirituality, developmentalism, and emergence. At its core is the desire to assist in the cultivation of a more developed and evolved human being. It is my belief that this cultivation will usher in a new Renaissance, one that will see the dawning of a humane and more peaceful world.

One

The Mind of Science

Diversity and the Common Cold
"I love the doctors—they are such dears;
But must they spend such years and years
Investigating such a lot
Of illnesses which no one's got,
When everybody, young and old,
Is frantic with the common cold?
And I will only eat my hat
If they know anything of that!"[1]

The common cold is one of the leading causes of illness in the United States. Every year about 25 million people visit their family doctors with the common cold, resulting in 20 million days of absence from work and 22 million days of absence from school.[2]

Despite great advances in certain aspects of modern medicine (what I also will call biomedicine), the common cold continues to be a great burden on society in terms of human suffering and economic losses.[3] And as Alan Herbert's poem above implies, the cure for the common cold has escaped the grasp of modern medicine. The reason is the diverse nature of viruses that cause colds. One quarter of all colds are still without proven cause. The recent discovery of human metapneumovirus suggests that many other common cold-causing viruses still remain undiscovered.[4]

The inability of biomedicine to deal effectively with the common cold is symptomatic of the problems biomedicine faces, problems based on biomedicine's worldview of reductionism and linear determinism. This worldview has no place for diversity and complexity. Yet, diversity and complexity is the path that viruses travel on, and, for that matter, the path all life travels. Because of modern medicine's stubborn desire to uphold its worldview, it is facing some difficult challenges and will continue to do so far into the foreseeable future.

Although billions of dollars fuel the modern healthcare system, people are not getting healthier—the contrary seems to be the case. The theories and treatment strategies of biomedicine with regard to chronic illness have always been limited and remain so. Modern medicine continues to be largely ineffective in combating chronic, degenerative, and age-related illnesses.[5] Physicians understand this and universally acknowledge a crisis in health care.[6] Many physicians are unhappy because of the inherent frustrations of operating in a system that isn't working. Indeed, chronic depression is epidemic among doctors.[7] One physician writes, "There must be a frank acknowledgement of how much physicians are suffering today."[8] Another physician writes that the basic reason for biomedicine's profound crisis is that biomedicine has lost its way, if not its soul.[9]

Biomedicine, like most of the sciences, tends to view things from a reductionist perspective. Reductionism is the process of reducing complex data or phenomena to their simplest terms. In biomedicine the reductionist model presents human beings as nothing more than biochemical components. In science, reductionism tends to believe that all that exists is matter and energy moving predictably, linearly, and deterministically in space and time.[10]

SCIENCE AND PSYCHOPHYSICS

Science is not a monolithic field, and not all scientists are cut from the same cloth. There are many scientists, working in various disciplines, who view life from the submicroscopic to the macroscopic to the cosmic in a less reductionist light. These include both physical and social scientists. Physical scientists who see things in a different light use findings from the fields of quantum theory, complexity theory, systems theory, the science of emergence, modern physics, biology, biochemistry, medicine, and other fields to forge ahead and push forward to new frontiers.

Social scientists who see things in a different light use findings from psychology, sociology, and cognitive science, often times blending them in with observations of the overall cultural milieu to understand the workings of life.

Then, there are the interdisciplinary or integral thinkers, who may be developing the most mature, sophisticated, and advanced concepts. They integrate the findings from both the physical and social sciences and integrate them with understandings that have been developed over millennia by wisdom traditions and philosophers. In doing so they are attempting to merge understandings of the exterior and objective domains of science and nature with understandings of the interior and subjective domains of mind and consciousness. What motivates them is a desire to show that the universe does not rely solely on physical laws, but rather on psychophysical laws, or the interaction of mind and consciousness with nature.

In a universe predicated on psychophysical laws, the search for a theory of everything, which is the attempted unification of the four forces of nature—the strong nuclear force, the weak nuclear force, gravity, and electromagnetism—into a grand unification theory, would have to be expanded to encompass these laws. Some argue that a theory of everything will never be complete without the inclusion of consciousness, since consciousness is part of the landscape, even though it does not appear to derive from physical laws. As scientist David Chalmers writes:

> The existence of consciousness does not seem to be derivable from physical laws. Physicist Steven Weinberg defends physics by arguing that it might eventually explain what he calls the objective correlates of consciousness (that is, the neural correlates), but of course to do this is not to explain consciousness itself. If the existence of consciousness cannot be derived from physical laws, a theory of physics is not a true theory of everything. So a final theory must contain an additional component. A complete theory will have two components: physical laws, telling us about the behavior of physical systems from the infinitesimal to the cosmological, and what we might call psychophysical laws, telling us how some of those systems are associated with conscious experience. These two components will constitute a true theory of everything.[11]

SCIENTISM AND MENTAL MODELS

If a theory of everything were based on psychophysical laws, it would mean that modern science would need to adjust its approach accordingly. For the last few hundred years, the approach that science has been practicing is what is called scientism, which is the belief that the entire world can be fully explained in the language of objective processes. By explaining the world solely in terms of objective processes, science has become scientific materialism, in which the entire universe is explained purely by, and reduced to, physical laws. Yet, as David Chalmers pointed out, a universe described by only physical laws is not a true and complete picture of the universe.

And it is not just scientists who practice scientism. As philosopher Huston Smith pointed out, scientists do not have a monopoly on scientism.[12] "We have all stumbled into these constricting aspects of our contemporary view," he writes, "this is something that has happened for which all of us, we denizens of the modern world—we're all responsible for it."[13]

Moreover, underlying scientism's worldview are assumptions made that are taken for granted without question, assumptions about how the world operates. These assumptions create mental models that give scientists in particular, and people in general, a mental framework for how the workings of the world are to be comprehended.

Since mental models are deeply held images of how the world works, images that limit us to familiar ways of thinking and acting, they often conflict with new insights and can hold us back from putting these new insights into action.[14] Mental models can determine not only how we make sense of the world, but how we take action. "Although people do not always behave congruently with what they say," writes Chris Argyris, "they do behave congruently with their mental models."[15]

Scientism is the mental model contemporary scientists use, referred to by some as the "metaphysical foundations of modern science." In the foreword to the book, *New Metaphysical Foundations of Modern Science*, Jane Clark writes that the scientist E. A. Burtt wrote a seminal book in 1924 that made this point clearly:

> Burtt pointed out that behind the methodology of science, underpinning all its findings and theories, were a number of assumptions about the nature of the world and the way in which human beings can understand it—ontological and epistemological assumptions—which were neither articulated nor brought into question during the course of normal research. These he called the "metaphysical foundations" (not to be confused with the kind of meta-

physics found within the spiritual traditions) because they do not reside within the material world as such, nor can they be proven by empirical experiments, but they form the ground out of which all our conceptual ideas about the physical world arise.[16]

LOGICAL CONUNDRUMS AND INCOMPLETENESS

Even though science believes it is predicated on physical laws that describe objective processes, the historian of science Thomas Kuhn pointed out that scientific facts are instead embedded in cultural practices or paradigms.[17] Science operates within the context of the culture it exists in; it does not exist in a vacuum where pure absolute objectivity prevails.

In biomedicine, for example, physicians always base their diagnosis on assumptions within the context of their culture. In the United States, a reasonably healthy person with an enlarged spleen would be suspected of mononucleosis. In South America, this same person would be suspected of having Chagas' disease; in Ethiopia, Ewing's tumor. All these diagnoses would be correct. If an American physician were put in sub-Sahara Africa, or a Saudi physician in Nebraska, each would have trouble making proper diagnoses of their patients.[18] Because biomedicine operates within the context of the culture of which it is part, these physicians would be like fish out of water and not fully cognizant of the cultural mores of their host land.

It could be said that the illusion of absolute objectivity is one of the metaphysical foundations of modern science. As the philosopher and social theorist Ken Wilber (1949-) has written, "In order to assert that all truth is 'strictly empirical,' empiricists have to stand in intersubjective structures that their own theories cannot even account for. The linguistic assertion that all valid knowledge is empirical is not itself empirical, and thus in asserting their own position, they contradict themselves."[19]

In other words, the belief that all can be explained as objective processes is a mental construct; and if it is a mental construct, then it is a subjective belief; and if it is a subjective belief, then it lies outside the realm of objectivity and of physical laws explained by objective processes.

This conundrum of logic is similar to the liar's paradox that the ancient Greek philosophers and logicians devised. The liar's paradox goes like this: "Epimenides is a Cretan who says, 'All Cretans are liars.'" If Epimenides is telling the truth, then all Cretans are liars, so he is lying—which is a contradiction. If he is lying, then all Cretans are not liars and he may be telling the truth—which is also a contradiction.

The contradictory logic of both of these conundrums—the fact that both statements create infinite feedback loops of logic that one can never escape—was addressed by the mathematician Kurt Godel in his Incompleteness Theorem. In his theorem Godel was able to prove that rational thought by itself can never penetrate to the final ultimate truth because there are too many paradoxes and contradictions within the limitations of logic and rational thought.[20] If this is the case, then, scientism, by the virtue of the way its system obtains knowledge, will always be caught in a web of tangled logic, flaws, and contradictions, because of the peculiar limits of rational thought.

Many of the objective laws of science are flawed, such as the laws of thermodynamics. They are flawed because they are dealing with abstract concepts and not with a real world that is a living, breathing, open universe. Yet at the same time subjective experiences are considered unreliable and are denied at all costs in order to preserve the objectivity of science.[21] Science has thus painted itself into a corner of its own making. Its objective laws do not give a full and complete picture of the universe, yet it refuses to look beyond objective laws for answers.

OPENING UP THE FLOODGATES

Science has always been based on the networking of ideas and the evolution of new ideas based on prior concepts. Copernicus' theory of a heliocentric universe, Newton's theory of gravitation, Maxwell's theory of electromagnetism, Darwin's theory of evolution, Einstein's theory of relativity, quantum theory, and many others were all theories that evolved from earlier ideas. Indeed, the whole of human experience is predicated on what came before, be it ideas, cultural mores, behavioral patterns, or whatever. Indeed, not only the whole of human experience, but the entire realm of existence is predicated on what came before. Scientists now believe that all the atoms in the universe were created in the Big Bang, and that every atom in the body can trace its origin to the beginning of the universe. As the Koran states: "The universe is as close as the veins in your neck."

When Einstein formulated his special theory of relativity in 1905, it unlocked a floodgate of ideas that built on what Einstein had done, ideas that questioned the foundations of scientific materialism. These questions began with the development of quantum theory, with concepts promulgated by the likes of Erwin Shroedinger, Werner Heisenberg, Arthur Eddington, James Jeans, Niels Bohr, and others, which began to challenge the worldview of science. The physicists themselves recognized this fact and had much to say about it. Eddington offered this:

> In the world of physics we watch a shadowgraph performance of familiar life. The shadow of my elbow rests on the shadow table as the shadow ink flows over the shadow paper...The frank realization that physical science is concerned with a world of shadows is one of the most significant of recent advances.[22]

And Jeans had this to say:

> The essential fact is simply that all the pictures which science now draws of nature, and which alone seem capable of according with observational fact, are mathematical pictures...They are nothing more than pictures—fictions if you like, if by fiction you mean that science is not yet in contact with ultimate reality. Many would hold that, from the broad philosophical standpoint, the outstanding achievement of twentieth-century physics is not the theory of relativity with its welding together of space and time, or the theory of quanta with its present apparent negation of the laws of causation, or the dissection of the atom with the resultant discovery that things are not what they seem; it is the general recognition that we are not yet in contact with ultimate reality. We are still imprisoned in our cave, with our backs to the light, and can only watch the shadows on the wall.[23]

AN INTERCONNECTED UNIVERSE

The further expansion of quantum theory has led to new insights and developments in science within physics and other fields. Following the typical pattern of the evolution of ideas, new concepts and even new disciplines have been spawned from the wealth of new ideas that have been cultivated since Einstein's groundbreaking theory in 1905. As Arthur C. Clarke has commented, the early part of the twentieth century was an extraordinary period of revolutionary thought and experiment in science.[24] What has come out of this groundswell of knowledge is the understanding that at a fundamental level, there is a basic fundamental interconnectedness, wholeness, and oneness between all aspects of the universe.[25]

If this is so, the laws of nature should more readily reflect this. And if psychophysical laws are more capable of explaining nature than strictly physical laws, then it stands to reason that there is a connection between the physical world and mind and consciousness. Werner Heisenberg noted, "Natural science does not simply describe and explain nature; it is a part of the interplay between nature and ourselves; it describes nature as exposed to our method of questioning. This was a possibility Descartes could not have thought, but it makes the sharp separation between the world and the I impossible."[26]

If there is no sharp separation between the world and I, as Heisenberg postulated, this means the world is predicated on interconnectedness. And if, as Thomas Kuhn pointed out earlier, scientific facts and worldviews are embedded in cultural practices, then a science of interconnectedness will need to find a way to make a place for cultural habits and practices. It can even be said that a science of interconnectedness is the most complete theory of everything and that a theory of everything is not just a psychophysical model, but a psychophysical, cultural, and social model, more correctly called a biopsychosocial model, because it integrates the physical, mental, cultural, and social realms.

Some of the newer developing fields of science—systems theory, chaos theory, complexity theory, and the science of emergence—are disciplines that study this integration and interconnectedness, looking at the patterns of diversity that are universally seen throughout the landscape of life and then applying this knowledge to different domains. They use terminology, such as autopoiesis, self-organization, emergence, and nonlinear dynamics, to explain these patterns.

As noted earlier, it is integral thinkers who may have the broadest perspective since they combine concepts from these newer fields of science and incorporate them within a biopsychosocial model. In addition, they have a desire to press forward and embrace and understand the greater role of mind, consciousness, and even spirit within this framework. They are the ones asking the hard questions, such as, what is mind?; what is consciousness?; what is spirit?; and how do mind, consciousness, and spirit inform the biopsychosocial model?

An Interconnected Medicine

Since medicine is a branch of science, and science can be fit into this larger framework, then it stands to reason that medicine should fit into this larger framework as well. Medicine could then be expanded beyond its current status as a technological medicine. Instead of taking a reductionist approach, that views a person as the sum of that person's molecular and cellular processes, medicine can take the long view and see a person as the sum of their biopsychosocial and even spiritual realms. Modern medicine could then return to its roots as both an art and a science since traditional and indigenous systems of medicine have always understood healing to be both an art and science. Practitioners of traditional medicine have always regarded medicine as first and foremost a spiritual practice.[27]

If medicine were to take this approach, it would need to encompass the newer fields of science in its approach to the human body. Diversity, complexity, and emergence would be seen as properties to be encouraged, and it would be understood that these functions within the body parallel the workings of all aspects of the universe—from the submicroscopic, to the macroscopic, to the cosmic. A place would also have to be made for the role of mind and consciousness in the equation.

When medicine and healing are looked at from this broader perspective, the field of human potential becomes an important component. As to heal requires using one's healing potential, to use one's healing potential requires that one use one's human potential. Humans beings have much innate potential, of which very little ever gets utilized.

Towards A New Science of Healing and Human Potential

The worldview based on scientism and determinism that is leading society to a dead end needs to be replaced with a new worldview, a worldview that is starting to be developed and espoused by integral thinkers. This worldview can then be applied to many disciplines and areas of life.

In my work in the health care field, I have seen on many occasions the often disastrous repercussions and consequences of biomedical treatment. I believe these are due to the inherent weakness of the biomedical model: its basis in reductionism, its reliance on linear thinking, and its failure to incorporate human values. Biomedicine refuses to take into account the biopsychosocial aspects of health, mainly because it does not fit into the prevailing model of scientism that explains the world solely in terms of physical laws and objective processes. In the United States a hundred years ago, the physician knew the patient as a person, was familiar with the family, and had a sound notion of the patient's psychological and social stresses.[28] Unfortunately, that went by the wayside with the advent of modern medicine.

Fortunately, for the general public there is a system of medicine that pays attention to the individual and sees the patient as connected to a greater whole—the system of complementary medicine. Under the umbrella of complementary medicine are health providers of all different stripes—from acupuncturists to herbalists, chiropractors, homeopaths, massage therapists, energy healers, and mind-body medicine practitioners. Some may be physicians, but more often they are not. On the whole, they are competent, serious, professional, caring, knowledgeable, and well trained in their field. A report that studied why people use alternative medicine found that "Users of alternative health care find in alternative therapies an acknowledgment of the importance of treating illness within a larger context of spirituality and life meaning. The use of alternative care is part of a broader value orientation and set of cultural beliefs, one that embraces a holistic, spiritual orientation to life."[29]

Even though more than half of all Americans visit a practitioner of complementary medicine yearly, complementary medicine is still the stepchild of the medical system.[30] Biomedicine is still the prevailing approach, just as scientism is the prevailing approach in science.

Yet the system is broken—health care costs are prohibitively expensive and people are not getting healthier. At the same time, people are demanding a medical system that can take care of their health needs. Most of the current solutions to what is ailing the system involve containing runaway medical costs. While this is valid, this is still a quantitative approach, while what is more urgently needed is a qualitative approach. An entire new science of medicine and healing is what is needed.

Furthermore, because human potential is intrinsically tied into the human condition and to the ability for a person to use their own innate healing system, a new science of medicine and healing should also encompass this potential and see it as two sides of the same coin. Norman Cousins once wrote that human potentiality is the greatest untapped force on earth.[31]

To take the first step towards a new science of medicine, healing, and human potential, what is needed is what Edgar Mitchell, the former astronaut and founder of the Institute of Noetic Sciences, has suggested. To achieve new solutions, he says, "We need to think creatively, and we need to think out of the box—the box being the mindset that our society has taught us, both through science and culture."[32]

To reach these new solutions, new mental models need to be created in the spirit of what scientist Mitchell Feigenbaum suggested when he was making new discoveries in the chaos sciences during the 1980s—discoveries that demonstrated the limitations of the scientism model. Feigenbaum stated, "I needed to create a new intuition."[33] A new intuition is a new mental model, and it should be a model based on a true theory of everything, one that is inclusive of the new sciences, inclusive of philosophical and spiritual traditions, inclusive of the biopsychosocial realm, and inclusive of the realm of mind and consciousness. It should also be a model that looks at and evaluates our entire approach to education and learning because it is in the process of learning that more rigid mental models are reinforced, mental models that ultimately impede human potential.

If you find the new science of healing and human potential that I present in this book intriguing, you can visit the website www.quantum integralcenter.com to find out about a training program that applies this new science in a very practical manner.

Chapter Notes

1. Herbert, AP. "The common cold." In *Look Back and Laugh*. London: Methuen, 1960, 115-17.

2. Adams, PF, GE Hendershot and MA Marano. "Current estimates from the National Health Interview Survey." *Vital Health Statistics*. 10 (1999): 1996.

3. Heikkinen, Terho and Asko Jarvinen. "The common cold." *Lancet*. 361, no. 9351 (Jan. 4, 2003): 51-59.

4. Ibid.

5. Dossey, Larry. *Reinventing Medicine*. New York: HarperCollins Publishers, 1999: 21.

6. Lown, Bernard. *The Lost Art of Healing*. New York: Houghton Mifflin, 1996: xi.

7. Dossey, *Reinventing Medicine*, p. 229.

8. Sulmasy, Daniel P. "Is medicine a spiritual practice?" *Academic Medicine*. 74, no. 9 (Sept. 1999): 1003.

9. Lown, *The Lost Art of Healing*, p. xi.

10. Dixey, Richard. "Man, matter and metaphysics: Can we create a total science?" In Jane Clark and Willis Harman (eds.). *New Metaphysical Foundations of Modern Science*. Sausalito, CA: Institute of Noetic Sciences, p. 146.

11. Chalmers, David. "The puzzle of conscious experience." *Scientific American*. 273, no. 6 (June 1995): 80.

12. Smith, Huston. Beyond the Post-Modern Mind. Interview by Jeffrey Mishlove. *Thinking Allowed Productions*, 1998: 7. www.intuition.org/txt/smith.htm.

13. Ibid.

14. Senge, Peter. *The Fifth Discipline*. New York: Bantam Doubleday Dell, 1990: 174.

15. Argyris, Chris. *Reasoning, Learning, and Action: Individual and Organizational*. San Francisco: Josey-Bass, 1982: 79.

16. Clark, Jane. Foreword in Jane Clark and Willis Harman (eds.). *New Metaphysical Foundations of Modern Science*. Sausalito, CA: Institute of Noetic Sciences, 1994: x.

17. Kuhn, Thomas. *The Structure of Scientific Revolutions*. Chicago: University of Chicago Press, 1962.

18. Grim, Pamela. "Too close to Ebola." *Discover*. 24, no. 6 (June 2003): 43.

19. Wilber, Ken. *The Eye of Spirit*. Boston: Shambhala Publications, 1997: 24.

20. Rucker, Rudy. *Infinity and the Mind*. Princeton: Princeton University Press, 1995.

21. Ho, Mae-Wan. "Toward an Indigenous Western Science: Causality in the Universe of Coherent Space-Time Structures." In Jane Clark and Willis Harman (eds.). *New Metaphysical Foundations of Modern Science*. Sausalito, CA: Institute of Noetic Sciences, 1994: 181.

22. Eddington, Arthur. *The Nature of the Physical World*. New York: Macmillan, 1929: 282.

23. Jeans, James. *The Mysterious Universe*. Cambridge: Cambridge University Press, 1931: 111.

24. Jueneman, Frederic B. "Hyperspace." *R & D*. 37, no. 11 (August 1995): 55.

25. Harman, Willis. "Toward a Science of Wholeness." In Jane Clark and Willis Harman (eds.). *New Metaphysical Foundations of Modern Science*. Sausalito, CA: Institute of Noetic Sciences, 1994: 376.

26. Heisenberg, quoted in Jahn, Robert and Brenda Dunne. "The Spiritual Substance of Science." In Jane Clark and Willis Harman (eds.). *New Metaphysical Foundations of Modern Science*. Sausalito, CA: Institute of Noetic Sciences, 1994: 166.

27. Horrigan, Bonnie. "Papa Henry Auwae Po'okela la'au lapa'au: Master of Hawaiian medicine." *Alternative Therapies in Health and Medicine*. 6, no. 1 (Jan. 2000): 83.

28. Lown, *The Lost Art of Healing*, p. 140.

29. Astin, John. "Why patients use alternative medicine." *Journal of the American Medical Association*. 279, no. 19 (1998): 1549.

30. Eisenberg, David et al. "Trends in alternative medicine use in the United States, 1990-1997." *Journal of the American Medical Association*. 280, no. 18 (1998): 1569.

31. Cousins, Norman. "Tapping human potential." *Second Opinion*. 14, no. 1 (July, 1990): 68

32. Mitchell, Edgar. *A Workshop on Consciousness and Creativity*. Held in Saratoga Springs, NY, March 30, 2001.

33. Feigenbaum, quoted in Gleick, James. *Chaos: Making a New Science*. New York: Penguin Books, 1987:178.

Two

Healing and Human Potential

CAN PEOPLE CHANGE?

A shift in the worldview of medicine would require a change in perspective not only for those who practice medicine, but also for those who receive medical care. Yet how capable are people of change? Most are terrified of it, believing it to be painful and uncomfortable. Some say the reason for the inability of people to change is due to a "conspiracy of mediocrity" in the larger culture, one that expects people to conform to the average and discourages the intellectual rigor needed to discern and discriminate.[1] Others say the reason for the inability to change is that the predominant mental model demands one absolute, right answer and that these models are created by what society and its institutions—families, schools, communities, politicians, jobs, doctors, gurus, and others—teach.[2]

This type of mental model is what the educator and author Edward de Bono calls rock logic—a doctrine that states there is only one right, absolute answer. This is the hallmark of scientific determinism, a thinking similar to the predictability of a game of billiards, in which all trajectories can be plotted and known, or the predictability of a simple math problem, in which there is one and only one right answer.

Yet life is seldom like this. Much that occurs in life is unpredictable, indeterminable, uncertain, ambiguous, and complex. Things can be known and predicted up to a certain point, but then, somewhere along the line, there is a tendency for creative movement to occur. De Bono calls this approach to thinking water logic, one that allows for a degree of creative thinking.

Logic is important because there would be pure chaos without it. However, logical thinking can be narrow or it can be broad. The narrow approach manifests itself in scientism and biomedicine and sees things from a narrow spectrum. Broad logic encourages reflection and introspection and is willing to ask the hard questions that require discrimination and discernment. It tends to probe beyond accepted dogma. It is a way that has been used by the great sages, philosophers, and creative thinking scientists (such as Einstein) throughout the ages.

The great twelfth century Jewish physician and philosopher Moses Maimonides (1135-1204) called for the use of logic in medicine. But his admonition was for a broad logic, the antithesis of what is presently seen in biomedicine. The logic he called for left room for the cultivation of the art and mystery of science and healing. He understood that illness didn't occur in a vacuum because it was connected to other aspects of a person's life. He realized for a person to heal, the person's own healing capabilities would have to play an intrinsic role. He also understood that a person's healing capabilities were tied to their human potential as a whole and that the doctor's role at best was to help facilitate this potential.[3]

Maimonides was not the only person to talk about the power of the human potential. Many before and since have done the same, including Plato, Aristotle, Plotinus, Da Vinci, Voltaire, Goethe, Hegel, Emerson, William James, Rudolf Steiner, Abraham Maslow, and Martin Luther King. If this power can be tapped into, the power of human potential to heal and to use more of one's innate capacities will be seen as something everyone is capable of doing.

People do have the ability to change, just as people have the ability to change their mental models. There is nothing that says they need to be set in stone. It is just that people do not have the right tools for aiding change because people are not aware that these tools exist. There is the belief—the mental model—that change is difficult, if not impossible. A model of life that is based on linear determinism does not have the flexibility to allow for change, diversity, and uncertainty. However, a model based on a new science of healing and human potential allows for and indeed requires the ability to change. However, to achieve this model for individuals, and even society, requires a fundamental change in the worldview of science itself.

One of the main motivations that has guided me in my work has been the desire to see if it was possible to provide people with the tools to change their worldview. I have been teaching a class for the last few years on this subject, and it has led me to conclude that this is not as difficult a task as it might seem. My hope now is that as more people can be led to change their thinking, a new Renaissance might occur. This type of Renaissance would be one that would see the emergence of more creative thinkers in all fields—more spiritually aware people, more enlightened scientists, and the development of healing capabilities people previously did not know existed.

HEALING AND HUMAN POTENTIAL

The belief that there is a wellspring of potential intrinsic to humans is not a new phenomenon. Within the traditions of Buddhism, it was believed that the Buddha was awakened because he understood the evolution necessary to release the almost infinite potential within. His supreme accomplishment changed the way a large portion of humanity perceives reality, perhaps granting the human race the potential to unleash an unlimited future.[4] The founder of Taoism, Lao Tzu, and the early Zen Buddhists also had similar ideas about the human condition, believing that every person has an actualizing tendency that promotes growth, direction, and productivity. They believed there is something universal about this aspect of the human experience.[5]

The Greek philosopher Aristotle asserted that all living forms have a movement towards growth, change, and realization of their innate potential. He called this entelechy, the actualization of something's native potential. As an example, he posited that although an acorn is not an oak, it contains the potential to become one.[6]

In more recent times, the psychologist C. H. Patterson has stated that self-actualization is a concept that has universality because the drive for self-actualization is based on the physiological nature of all living forms.[7] A German-born psychiatrist, Kurt Goldstein, who coined the term self-actualization, believed that a person had to be viewed as a whole, what he called a "gestalt," and was greater than the sum of that person's parts. He felt that all human beings have an innate instinct to grow and to achieve their potential, that is, to self-actualize.[8]

The psychologist Abraham Maslow (1908-1970) made it his life's work to research the concept of self-actualization. He spent many years studying people who he felt fit this description, people who were using more of their innate potential. This allowed him to give a fuller definition of the term:

> Self-actualized people are working at something, something which is very precious to them—some calling or vocation in the old sense, the priestly sense. They are working at something which fate has called them to somehow and which they work at and which they love, so that the work-joy dichotomy in them disappears. One devotes his life to the law, another to justice, another to beauty or truth. All, in one way or another, devote their lives to the search for the ultimate values which are intrinsic, which cannot be reduced to anything more ultimate.[9]

Maslow also determined that these people had a certain way about them:

> A spurt in which the powers of the person come together in a particularly efficient and intensely enjoyable way, and in which he is more integrated and less split, more open for experience, more idiosyncratic, more perfectly expressive or spontaneous, or fully functioning, more creative, more humorous, more ego-transcending, more independent of his lower needs, etc. He becomes in these episodes more truly himself, more perfectly actualizing his potentialities, closer to the core of his Being, more fully human....What seems to distinguish those individuals I have called self-actualizing people, is that in them these episodes seem to come more frequently, and intensely and perfectly than in average people.[10]

Maslow's research helped spawn an entire movement, known as the human potential movement. The writer George Leonard helped spread the movement in the mid-1960s while a senior editor of *Look* magazine. Leonard did extensive research into the education system for an article he wrote, "Revolution in Education." In the article Leonard discussed human potential: "Ever since the human race first learned to wonder, men and women have been haunted by this irrepressible dream: that the limits of human ability lie beyond the boundaries of the imagination; that every human being uses only a fraction of his abilities; that there must be some way for everyone to achieve far more of what is truly theirs to achieve. History's greatest prophets, mystics, and saints have dreamed even more boldly, saying that all men are somehow one with God."[11]

During the course of his research Leonard spent time with leading psychologists and brain researchers, asking them why most people don't live up to their possibilities. "They all agreed that most of the innate capacity of most people is routinely squandered," he wrote. "It was clear that our mode of education itself was a major cause of this tragic waste."[12] The magazine received over 100 letters from readers, which essentially said, "That's what we really need to do, focus upon the human potential."[13]

THE EDUCATIONAL SYSTEM

What Leonard discovered in his research on education was that it was the education system itself that was playing a key role in suppressing human potential:

> It must be said that the typical first grade experience probably alters the brain of your child even more than would mind-altering drugs, doing untold violence to his potential as a lifelong learner. "Tragedy" is a strong word, but I can think of no other to describe what happens to most children during the early elementary years....Go into a kindergarten room. By and large, the five-year-olds are spontaneous, unique. Tell them to dance, and they move naturally with a sort of unorganized grace. Read them a story, and their eyes give you back its suspense, fear, laughter. We like to say their faces light up (a particularly telling phrase), and when we look into this illumination, we are not ashamed to let our own faces glow in return. All of this, we assume, is a natural condition of the young.

> Walk down the hall to a fourth-grade classroom. Very quickly, you will notice that something has been lost. Not so many eyes are alight. Not so many responses surprise you. Too many bodies and minds seem locked in painful self-awareness. This, too, we carelessly attribute to the natural order. It's just part of growing up. But is it really? Is it really necessary for the human animal to lose its spontaneity and imagination as it gains in knowledge and technique? Must we shed the brightness of childhood as we put on the armor plating of age?[14]

Leonard proposed using time more efficiently in school, and with the time saved, cultivating human potential. "Every child can learn to read, to write, to spell, to manipulate quantities, to learn all the hard stuff of present day schooling—in less than one-third the present time....We can take that extra two-thirds of present school time available to us right now and get on with the most exhilarating experiment in man's history: to help every child become, in his own way, an artist; to help every child become, in his own way, a genius; to see just how far toward ecstasy and accomplishment every human being can go."[15]

The education system plays a major role in the repression of human potential. With everyone compelled to go through the education system, it is no small wonder so few Einsteins, Da Vincis, Edisons, Faradays, and other brilliant thinkers who have done much to illuminate the world have emerged.

Take the case of Michael Faraday (1791-1867), the well-known nineteenth century scientist, who was the first to show the relationship between electricity and magnetism. In 1831, on a hunch, he tested to see what would happen if he spun a copper disk between the two poles of a horseshoe magnet. Faraday was shocked to find that this device actually generated electricity.[16] Einstein said of Faradays' discovery, "This device was an audacious mental creation, which we owe chiefly to the fact that Faraday never went to school, and therefore preserved the rare gift of thinking freely."[17]

Even though the education system can repress the ability to think freely, many a person has had a teacher who opened their mind and changed their life. Often this teacher was a maverick, someone who went against the grain of the system. In a magazine article entitled, "The Teacher

Who Opened My Mind," Mark Edmundson reminisced about the maverick teacher who came to his high school to teach philosophy and in the process changed his life.[18] He played football for the high school team, had "never read a book all the way through that was not about football," and took the class because "it seemed an agreeable enough way of wasting time."[19]

The class began by reading Durant, then turned its focus to Plato, Aristotle, Leibniz, Kant, and Bertrand Russell. The teacher then switched gears and had the students reading Albert Camus, Ken Kesey, Sigmund Freud, and Herman Hesse. He had them sit in a circle and encouraged the free flow of ideas. He brought in music—Billie Holiday, Mozart, the Velvet Underground—and art books, read poems, and had guest speakers. By the spring the class was held outside, much to the chagrin of the school administration, who feared that if they let this teacher do it, then everyone would want to do it. This teacher held his ground, asking the principal, "What if everyone held class outside on sunny days? Suppose that happened?" The principal relented.

> And from there, Lears [the teacher] went on to draw a picture of life at Medford High School that had people outside on the vast lawn talking away about books and ideas and one thing and another, hanging out, being lazy, being absorbed, thinking hard from time to time, and reveling in the spring. It was Woodstock and Socrates' agora fused, and Lears spun it out for us, just as he had for the principal. What if that happened, he asked us? How tragic would it be? We went outside whenever we chose to after that. It was very odd: I had been at Medford High for three years and I had never seen the principal lose a round.[20]

The teacher lasted only that one year at the high school, but in that year he made a strong and indelible impression on those he encountered. Edmundson recollected that Lears "pushed open the door to other worlds and other minds."[21]

As the above story implies, the blossoming of human potential often is cultivated and encouraged by someone. A special teacher can play such a strong role in the shaping of the human mind. Unfortunately, this cultivation process is usually not part of the educational process, and so much of human potential gets squelched from an early age. The writer James Agee understood the problem. "I believe that every human being is potentially capable, within his 'limits,' of fully 'realizing' his potentialities," Agee wrote. "That this, his being cheated and choked of it, is infinitely the ghastliest, commonest, and most inclusive of all the crimes of which the human world can accuse itself....I know only that murder is being done against nearly every individual on the planet."[22]

HUMAN POTENTIAL

In the mid-1960s, George Leonard, having researched and written about the relationship between human potential and the education system, was now ready to hone in on the subject of human potential, and *Look* magazine gave him total autonomy to do so. He spent seven months criss-crossing the country and interviewing 37 leading experts—psychiatrists, psychologists, brain researchers, theologians, and philosophers—on the subject of human potential. He found that "Not one of them said we were using more than 10% of our capacity. In later years, I came to realize that was a very conservative estimate—we're using about 1% I would guess. Maybe less."[23]

During the course of his research, Leonard made the acquaintance of Michael Murphy, the founder and director of the then fledgling Esalen Institute in Big Sur, California. Esalen ran educational programs for adults under the banner, "Human Potentialities." Murphy and Leonard immediately hit it off and began a friendship that has continued to this day. Together, they put forth the idea that there should be a human potential movement.[24]

Over the years this movement has gone through many fits and starts, peaks and valleys, going from a vehicle ripe for narcissism (leading to the 1970s being derisively coined "The Me Decade") to a vehicle for serious transformation on many levels and domains—the personal, cultural, and social.

The model for transformation and change that the human potential movement has encouraged is one that has also been adopted by business and industry, social organizations, and political leaders and statesmen such as Nelson Mandela, Vaclav Havel, and Jimmy Carter. This model reflects what Leonard and Murphy had in mind from the start: "We had in mind not just the emotional side of human experience. We had the idea of integral transformation—of mind, body, soul, and heart."[25] Nowadays, Leonard calls it less a human potential movement and more "the full development of human resources." He goes on to say, "Human resources are undeveloped, almost infinite. We could start a program on the development of human potential that would create adventures that would make the winning of the West seem pale indeed."[26]

SELF-HEALING

One area in which the full development of human resources and human potential is not fully understood is the capacity for self-healing. Just as one might ask what the limits of human potential might be, one might also ask the same question for the capacity of healing. Is there an infinite potential, a wellspring of healing capabilities within an individual that, if tapped, can play an important role in that person's ability to heal?

Hippocrates, the father of Western medicine, viewed the treatment of disease as a dual process. One part was represented by systematic medicine; the other part was the full activation of the patient's own healing system.[27] Norman Cousins learned about his innate healing system when he recovered from a very serious and life-threatening ailment, ankylosing spondylitis, a crippling and life-threatening disease of the connective tissue. Cousins was completely paralyzed and given just a few months to live, but through the power of his own natural healing system he recovered, and then went on to write about it in his best seller *Anatomy of an Illness*. In an interview Cousins stated his central claim about healing and why biomedical practitioners know so little about it:

> First, there is such a thing as a healing system. Unfortunately, the healing system is not part of a great deal of medical education. In medical textbooks, for example, you're not going to find very much in the index under healing system. You'll find listings for all the other systems but none for the healing system. And that unfortunately is an accurate indicator that the healing system is not sufficiently appreciated or understood. Yet if Franz Inglefinger is right in believing 85 percent of all illnesses to be self-limiting, something must be happening, and that

> something should have a name. I'm pretty sure that heal-
> ing system is about the best we can come up with, but why
> isn't it taught as such?…We spend so much time getting
> to know bugs that we've lost sight of people.[28]

Regardless of what medical students are taught, or not taught, about a healing system and what they come to believe, or not believe, once they are full-fledged medical doctors, they encounter substantial evidence that there is a healing system within the body that can affect health. All traditions of natural healing and medicine are predicated on the fact that the body has an innate potential to self-heal from any ailment and that all that is necessary for this to occur is for the healing system to be catalyzed.

When a person is able to utilize this self-healing system, the cure is often considered a spontaneous remission or miracle cure. Frequently medical science will dismiss these occurrences with pejorative comments such as, "I think you'd have a better chance of getting struck by lightning than of having a spontaneous remission of cancer."[29]

On the other hand, some biomedical scientists are more open to the possibility of these occurrences, and willing to reflect on its implications for the future: "The rare but spectacular phenomenon of spontaneous remission of cancer patients persists in the annals of medicine," wrote the late scientist and author Lewis Thomas. "A fascinating mystery, but at the same time a solid basis for hope in the future: if several hundred patients have succeeded in doing this sort of thing, eliminating vast numbers of malignant cells on their own, the possibility that medicine can learn to accomplish the same thing at will is surely within reach of imagining."[30]

It may be that the potential to self-heal is a subset of the range of the human potential and healing may be one aspect of this potential. For those who believe in the infinite potential of the human condition, acceptance of self-healing capacities is easy. Indeed, some human potential advocates are attempting to make it a core component of the medical system. But for those who subscribe to the system of scientism and medical determinism, there is no place for the possibility of a human healing system capable of healing the human condition of various ailments, because it is believed that all sickness, and all cures have a basis only in physicality. Let's now take a closer look at the system of scientific and medical logic that prevails in Western culture.

Chapter Notes

1. Kimura, Yasuhiko. "A philosopher of change." An interview by Carter Phipps. *What is Enlightenment?* No. 22 (Fall/Winter 2002): 34.

2. Mitchell, Edgar. *A Workshop on Consciousness and Creativity.* Held in Saratoga Springs, NY, March 30, 2001.

3. Bloch, Sidney. "Moses Maimonides' contribution to the biopsychosocial approach in clinical medicine." *Lancet.* 358, no. 9284 (Sept. 8, 2001): 832.

4. Ortner, Jon. *Where Every Breath is a Prayer.* New York: Stewart, Tabori, and Chang, 1996: 106.

5. Chang, Raylene and Richard C. Page. "Characteristics of the self-actualized person: Visions from the east and west." *Counseling and Values.* 36, no. 1 (Oct. 1991): 10.

6. Rohmann, Chris. *A World of Ideas.* New York: Ballantine Books, 1999: 27.

7. Patterson, C. H. *The Therapeutic Relationship: Foundations for an Eclectic Psychotherapy.* Belmont, CA: Brooks/Cole, 1985: 37.

8. Schwartz, Tony. *What Really Matters: Searching for Wisdom in America.* New York: Bantam, 1995: 88.

9. Maslow, Abraham. *The Farther Reaches of Human Nature.* New York: Penguin Books, 1971: 42.

10. Maslow, Abraham. *Toward A Psychology of Being.* New York: Van Nostrand Reinhold, 1968: 97.

11. Leonard, George. *Education and Ecstasy.* Berkeley: North Atlantic Books, 1968: 24.

12. Ibid, p. x.

13. Leonard, George. "Human Potential: From Esalen to Mainstreet." Interview by Russell E. DiCarlo. *HealthWorld Online,* 1996: 1 www.healthy.net/asp/templates/interview.asp?id=293&headertitle=conversations+.

14. Leonard, *Education and Ecstasy*, pp. 110-11.

15. Ibid, p. 116.

16. Osborn, Alex F. *Applied Imagination: Principles and Procedures of Creative Problem-Solving.* New York: Charles Scribner and Sons, 1953: 88-89.

17. Ibid, p. 45.

18. Edmundson, Mark. "The teacher who opened my mind." *Utne Reader.* 115 (Jan.- Feb. 2003): 74-79.

19. Ibid, p. 74.

20. Ibid, pp. 78-79.

21. Ibid, p. 76.

22. Agee, quoted in Leonard, *Education and Ecstasy*, p. 24.

23. Leonard, "Human Potential: From Esalen to Mainstreet," p.1.

24. Ibid.

25. Ibid, p. 2.

26. Leonard, George. *Transforming Human Nature*. Interview by Jeffrey Mishlove. Thinking Allowed Productions, 1998: 9. www.intuition.org/txt/smith.htm.

27. Cousins, Norman. "Healer Within." In *The Parabola Book of Healing*. New York: Continuum Publishing, 1994: 125.

28. Cousins, Norman. "Tapping human potential." *Second Opinion*. 14, no. 1 (July, 1990): 57.

29. Hall, Stephen S. "Cheating fate." *Health Magazine*. 6, no. 2 (April 1992): 39.

30. Thomas, Lewis. "Self-regulation through imagery. Part 2: Visualization and cancer therapy." In *Norris, P. Newsletter of the International Society for the Study of Subtle Energies and Energy Medicine*. 3, no. 2 (1992):2.

Three

Medicine and Aristotelian/Scientific Logic

Scientific logic is considered an Aristotelian logic, based on the formulations of the Greek philosopher Aristotle (384-322 BCE). His system of logic was mostly used unimpeded for the next 2,000 years. Considered to be the father of modern science, Aristotle predicated his system of classical or formal logic on the syllogism, in which, given two premises, a certain conclusion or inference can be made.[1] One example is, "All men are mortal; Socrates is a man; therefore, Socrates is mortal." Another example is, "All trees are made of wood; an oak is a tree; therefore, all oaks are made of wood."[2]

Aristotle was able to show that a systematic investigation into the nature of life should be based on a course of inquiry that progressively breaks things down to smaller and smaller components that would allow for a logical and disciplined study of the true nature of the world.[3]

Aristotle's system of inquiry lasted until the seventeenth century when Francis Bacon (1561-1626) advocated the addition of experience and induction as important components in the search for knowledge. Bacon's system of scientific investigation became the basis of the modern scientific method. The scientific method as developed by Bacon claimed that any valid knowledge must be supported by testing and confirmation and must aim to achieve objective results relatively free of guesswork and the influence of personal or cultural biases. The principles of the scientific method still form the basis of most research in the natural and social sciences.[4]

Bacon had a bias against the natural world, believing that nature was unreliable and must not be allowed to play a role in the scientific method. In a world that was increasingly seen as deterministic and predictable, nature was viewed as wild and unpredictable, needing to be manipulated and subjugated in order to be brought under control. Nature represented not just the natural world, but all things subjective and not easily quantified, including personal beliefs, emotions and aesthetics.[5] Because he advocated total objectivity, he felt the inclusion of nature would bias the scientist. Thus, he made such statements as nature had to be "hounded in her wanderings," "bound into service," and "made a slave." She was to be "put into constraint," and the aim of the scientist was to "torture nature's secrets from her."[6] In addition, Bacon is credited with first using the term "disciplines" to connote the various branches of the natural sciences. He used it in accordance with his injunction to discipline the imagination for the good of scientific inquiry.[7]

Thus was created scientism, the worldview of the western world. It is a linear determinism, based on a world that can be understood only by measuring its objective processes. To achieve this comprehension, the world is reduced to smaller and smaller components via reductionism, tending to see all fundamental particles working together predictably and mechanistically, as if in a factory.

THE BIOMEDICAL MODEL

From this paradigm the biomedical model has evolved. According to this model, the human body is regarded as a machine that can be analyzed in terms of its parts. Disease is seen as the malfunctioning of biological mechanisms which are studied from the point of view of cellular and molecular biology, so that the doctor's role is to intervene, either physically or chemically, to correct the malfunctioning of a specific mechanism.[8]

In this biomedical approach every cause should have a predictable effect and, likewise, a predictable cure. The human being is seen as a collection of organs, tissues, and other components into which it can be reduced. The whole is considered nothing more than the sum of its parts. In this way of thinking every cause that leads to a predictable effect and has a predictable cure can be taken care of easily. There should be no post-surgical complications, nor post-surgical recurrences of the original problems. Also, all drugs should take care of the problem being treated, and all side effects of drugs should be known and easily catalogued. In this model there is no place for the effects of consciousness and the mind on the body because consciousness is seen as nothing but the result of brain processes. This is the medical model that medical students learn and practice once they become biomedical practitioners, unless they are willing to expand their worldview.

Rachel Naomi Remen, a physician who learned some important lessons about healing when she underwent her own serious health problems, wrote a book, *Kitchen Table Wisdom: Stories That Heal*, which is a series of thoughtful and reflective essays about the medical profession. One essay in the book captures the essence of the biomedical mindset:

> As a pediatric intern, I was a secret baby kisser. This was so flagrantly 'unprofessional' I was careful not to be discovered. Late at night under the guise of checking a surgical dressing or an IV, I would make solo rounds on the ward and kiss the children good night. If there was a favorite toy or blanket, I would be sure it was close, and if someone was crying I would even sing a little. I never mentioned this dimension of my health care to anyone. I felt the other residents, mostly men, might think less of me for it.[9]

One evening Remen was talking to a patient's father in the corridor, when she glanced over his shoulder and saw Stan, her chief resident, bend over the crib of a little girl with leukemia and kiss her on the forehead. "In that moment," she writes, "I realized that others too might be struggling to extend themselves beyond an accepted professionalism to express a natural caring." She thought that perhaps there was a way to talk about these things, even to support one another.

One night when she and Stan were waiting to be called to the operating room for a C-section, she told him what she had seen and that it had meant something important to her. "Although we were alone in the doctors' lounge, Stan denied the whole thing. We dropped the subject in embarrassment."

For the rest of the year they worked together, thirty-six hours on call and twelve hours off and became trusted colleagues, good friends, and even occasional drinking buddies, "but we never mentioned the incident again."

Remen writes that Stan's integrity was almost legendary. He would never have fudged a piece of lab data or said he had read an article when he hadn't. But he would have had to step past their entire professional image and training to admit his heartfelt reaction to that little girl. It was just not professional behavior. "I stopped kissing the babies then," she writes, "It did not seem worth the risk."

She thinks that in some ways, a medical training is "like a disease. It would be years before I would fully recover from mine."[10]

Remen's story does not negate the significant and stunning achievements of biomedicine. Antibiotics and other medications, vaccines, enhanced surgical techniques, and lifesaving emergency measures are important aspects of this legacy. It is just that in its quest for knowledge biomedicine has assumed an omnipotence, believing that all diseases can and should be cured only according to its medical model. And its model is tilting even more in the direction of medical determinism, further removing subjectivity from the equation.

The new gold standard in biomedicine is the outcomes movement, also known as evidence-based medicine. Its aim is to have biomedicine rely exclusively on efficacies that are established through randomized double blind studies, as opposed to clinical experience. The goal of this approach is to purge "intuition, unsystematic clinical experience, and physiological rationale" from medical care.[11] Furthermore, according to evidence-based medicine, a physician's experience contributes little to, and may actually subvert, medical knowledge.[12] When the founder of evidence-based medicine, David Sackett, was asked to comment on the artful nature of clinical medicine, he replied, "Art kills."[13]

Fortunately, not all biomedicine practitioners are enthralled with this model, which in essence is the next logical step of a medicine based on scientism. One physician, writing in a medical journal, stated:

> There was another altogether more sympathetic figure—the repository of a wide clinical wisdom not available in books. This is the experienced clinician as hero. Their authority derives from experience and clarity of both thought and exposition. I think anyone who has gasped for air in a darkened auditorium under the crushing weight of a mountain of PowerPoint bar charts will

acknowledge that detail more often obscures truth than reveals it. The trouble with evidence-based medicine is the sheer undigested bulk of it, and its relative crudity as an instrument for analyzing something as complex as the practice of medicine. I still feel the need for medical heroes to guide me with simple conclusions, even though I know that that simplicity is the outcome of technical subtlety. But my heroes are active clinicians rather than experts on bar charts. For me, a simple clinical aphorism is usually worth a thousand abstracts. It is summed up in a quotation I have always ascribed, somewhat implausibly, to Yogi Bear: in theory there is no difference between theory and practice; in practice there is.[14]

Another group of writers, with tongue partly in cheek, ascribe the machinations of the evidence-based medicine movement as akin to a religious movement. They published a report in which they declared that evidence-based medicine has 10 Commandments:

1. Thou shalt treat all patients according to the EBMcookbook, without concern for local circumstances, patients' preferences, or clinical judgement

2. Thou shalt honor thy computerized evidence based decision support software, humbly entering the information that it requires and faithfully adhering to its components

3. Thou shalt put heathen basic scientists to the rack until they repent and promise henceforth to randomize all mice, materials, and molecules in their experiments

4. Thou shalt neither publish nor read any case reports, and punish those who blaspheme by uttering personal experiences

5. Thou shalt banish the unbelievers who partake in qualitative research, and force them to live among basic scientists and other heathens

6.   Thou shalt defrock any clinician found treating a patient without reference to all research published more than 45 minutes before a consultation

7.   Thou shalt reward with a bounty any medical student who denounces specialists who use expressions such as "in my experience"

8.   Thou shalt ensure that all patients are seen by research librarians, and that physicians are assigned to hand searching ancient medical journals

9.   Thou shalt force to take mandatory retirement all clinical experts within a maximum of 10 days of their being declared experts

10.   Thou shalt outlaw contraception to ensure that there are adequate numbers of patients to randomize[15]

To remove clinical experience from medical care and replace it purely with objective data is at the heart of evidence-based medicine and, more importantly, at the heart of scientism. It could be said that evidence-based medicine is the apex of biomedical scientism. Yet, as noted earlier, if science is embedded in cultural and social values, pure objectivity will never be achieved because personal and professional biases will always permeate judgement.

A case in point is advertising for prescription drugs. Because of the effect of the evidence-based medicine movement, the drug industry incorporates bibliographical references to clinical trials that endorse their products in their ads.[16] Since randomized clinical trials or systemic reviews of the leading trials are seen as the highest level of scientific evidence,[17] quotes used scientifically to reinforce the efficacy, safety, or other positive aspects of the drug being promoted are most often drawn from these trials.

Since evidence-based medicine promotes data based on trials and objective findings, it should follow that drug advertising that refers to clinical trials should be seen as following a course of action that is in line with evidence-based medicine. Yet, using the pretext of objective data, drug companies are manipulating facts for their own purposes. A recent investigation by the U. S. General Accounting Office found that many drug companies have repeatedly disseminated misleading advertisements for prescription drugs, even after being cited for violations, and millions of people see these deceptive ads before the government tries to halt them.[18] It seems obvious that even seemingly pure, objective data can be manipulated to meet the needs of a person or party who has a point or agenda to get across, or a dollar to be made.

Objective data can be organized in such a way that it supports either side of an argument. Ultimately, objective data can be used as a tool to stifle dissent and to support the prevailing worldview. In other words, Aristotelian and scientific logic is often used to maintain an existing dogma. History has seen this occur throughout the ages. Just one example of this is the many people who were burned at the stake at the height of the Inquisition for questioning Church doctrine.

While the collection of objective data by clinical trials is certainly important, both the biomedical model and scientific model need to be broadened to include the subjective realm, the realm where kissing babies is valued and seen as part of the norm. Human interaction is at the core of the healing experience, as it is at the core of all experience. As physician Bernard Lown writes:

> Our health care system is breaking down because the medical profession has been shifting its focus away from healing, which begins with listening to the patient. The reasons for this shift include a romance with mindless technology, which is embraced in large measure as a means for maximizing income. Since it is uneconomic to spend much time with patients, diagnosis is performed by exclusion, which opens floodgates for endless tests and procedures. Malpractice suits should be viewed as mere pustules on the physiognomy of a sick health care system. They are not what ails medicine in the United States, they are the consequence. The medical care system will not be cured until the patient once again becomes central to the doctor's agenda.[19]

Chapter Notes:

1. Glenn, Jim. *Scientific Genius: The Twenty Greatest Minds.* Avenel, NJ: Crescent Books: 8.

2. Rohmann, Chris. *A World of Ideas.* New York: Ballantine Books, 1999: 26.

3. Glenn, *Scientific Genius: The Twenty Greatest Minds*, p. 9.

4. Rohmann, *A World of Ideas*, p. 354.

5. Capra, Fritjof. *The Turning Point.* New York: Bantam, 1982: 40.

6. Merchant, Carolyn. *The Death of Nature.* New York: Harper & Row, 1980: 169.

7. Goodwin, Brian C. "Toward A Science of Qualities." In Jane Clark and Willis Harman (eds.). *New Metaphysical Foundations of Modern Science.* Sausalito, CA: Institute of Noetic Sciences, 1994: 238.

8. Capra, *The Turning Point,* p. 123.

9. Remen, Rachel Naomi. *Kitchen Table Wisdom: Stories That Heal.* New York: Riverhead Books, 1996: 61-62.

10. Ibid.

11. Evidence-based Medicine Working Group, cited in Tannenbaum, Sandra J. "Evidence and expertise: The challenge of the outcomes movement to medical professionalism." *Academic Medicine.* 74, no. 7 (July 1999): 759.

12. Ibid, p. 758.

13. Zuger, Alan. "New way of doctoring: By the book." *The New York Times.* (Dec. 16, 1997): B11.

14. Barraclough, Kevin. "Medical heroes." *British Medical Journal.* 326, no. 7380 (Jan. 11, 2003): 111.

15. "EBM: Unmasking the Ugly Truth." *British Medical Journal.* 325, no. 7378 (Dec. 21, 2002): 1496-97.

16. Villanueva, Pilar, Salvador Peiro, Julian Librero and Inmaculada Pereiro. "Accuracy of pharmaceutical advertisements in medical journals." *Lancet.* 361, no. 9351 (Jan. 4, 2003): 27.

17. Sackett, DL, WS Richardson, W Rosenberg and RB Haynes. *Evidence-Based Medicine: How to Practice and Teach.* London: Churchill-Livingstone, 1997.

18. Pear, Robert. "Investigators find repeated deception in ads for drugs." *The New York Times Online*, Dec. 4, 2002: 1. http://Query.nytimes.com/search/restricted/article?res=F00C1FF83C5F0C778CDDAB0994DA4.

19. Lown, Bernard. *The Lost Art of Healing.* New York: Houghton Mifflin, 1996: 156-57

Four

The Expansion of Medical Determinism

As much as biomedicine would like to believe it is the final word in scientific understanding, this is not the case. Science is predicated on logic, and as seen earlier, the roots of this logic is Aristotelian logic, breaking things down into component parts. While this by itself is valid, and remains valid to this day, the nature of logic runs deeper.

The study of logic is something that has been taken up by philosopher-scientists from time immemorial. Many have made statements about what constitutes logic. For instance, the mathematician Gottlob Frege (1848-1925) said, "To discover truths is the task of all sciences; it falls to logic to discern the laws of truth."[1] The philosopher Ludwig Wittgenstein (1889-1951) said, "Logic deals with every possibility and possibilities are its facts."[2] And the mathematician and logician Kurt Godel (1906-78) said, "Logic is the theory of pure concepts."[3]

If logic is what the three men above say it is, then someone searching for the logic of anything has to be willing to search for the ultimate truth. This means that any scientist, or thinker, who adheres to the laws of logic, would always have to be willing to search for meaning, look under the surface, stubbornly refuse to accept dogmas, and not accept things at face value. If this were the case and biomedicine abided by the rules of logic, then biomedicine would also have to be willing to dig deeper into the laws of truth and accept that its worldview might not be the final word.

GODEL AND INCOMPLETENESS

It was Godel's Incompleteness Theorem in 1931 that shattered the concept of a logic that adhered to closed thinking, a thinking that believed its way was the absolute truth, as do scientism and biomedicine. In his theorem Godel demonstrated that any sufficiently rich deductive system will generate statements that are meaningful but unprovable within the system. He showed that a sufficiently developed system cannot ever be complete and closed. It must either be complete and inconsistent, or incomplete and consistent,[4] as is the case with the statement "Epimenides is a Cretan who says, 'All Cretans are liars.'"

Godel showed conclusively that what is true and what is provable are not the same thing ever at all. His work revealed that there is an eternally unbridgeable gap between what is true (and can even be seen to be true) within a given logical framework or system and what can be actually proven by logical means using that same system.[5] Even though Godel's main work was in mathematics, his theorem was shown to have relevancy and application to the universe beyond mathematics—science, medicine, law, economics, religion, and even to general, everyday events.

Ultimately, what Godel was saying was that a sufficiently rich system must be open-ended in order to find true meaning, and the only way to prove a proposition was to go outside the system. Before Godel it was possible to claim that in our universe all was knowable, all problems could be solved, and everything could be learned.

Charles Duell was part of this way of thinking. He was the director of the U.S. Patent Office, who suggested in 1899 that the government close the office because everything that could be invented had been invented.[6] Over a 100 years ago one of the Deans of Harvard University said science was nearly complete and tried to discourage students from going into it, since he felt there was nothing more to learn.[7]

Since Godel, the opposite is true—that it is impossible to know everything, and it will never be possible to know everything, because the universe is open-ended and infinite. Indeed, Godel's theorem "shows that human thought is more complex and less mechanical than anyone had ever believed."[8] John von Neumann, himself a great mathematician, wrote that "Godel's achievement in modern logic is singular and monumental...a landmark which will remain visible in space and time."[9]

In his book *Infinity and the Mind*, the mathematician Rudy Rucker called Godel "the greatest logician of the century."[10] Some even consider Godel the greatest logician since Aristotle.[11] This might very well be true. Aristotle's achievement showed us how to methodically build a case, and demonstrated the superiority of the use of logic, but no one ever went beyond what Aristotle did. Francis Bacon refined Aristotle's work and cast it in a new light, but did not create a totally new worldview. This is Godel's stunning achievement: he expanded the concept of logic and broadened and changed the worldview of linear determinism. His portrait of the universe is one that shows the universe to be open-ended and infinite, one in which knowledge may become significant and extensive but never complete. These findings run parallel to current cosmological findings, which show that the universe is infinite and changing and encompasses a broadness that includes every possible history within the sum totality of creation.[12]

A universe ruled by Godelian laws cannot be a clockwork universe because a clockwork universe runs on mechanical and predictable laws that are always known. As Albert Einstein once said, "Knowledge is limited; imagination is more important than knowledge; imagination encircles the world."

A universe in which all is believed to be knowable tends towards dogmatic thinking. As the scientist and writer George Zebrowski wrote:

> Dogmas are the enemies of Godel's universe because they attempt to end all discussions and tests of truth; they are totalitarian viruses for the mind, preventing the creative growth that Godel's proof implies is possible. Godel's universe is not totalitarian, yet it does not deny our need for order and explanation. Its liberating incompleteness suggests that we can, in time, achieve our dreams; vast if not final knowledge; ongoing civilization; perhaps even endless life and a redemption of the past. It only asks us to reenact all forms of completeness, or closure, which is totalitarian (clockwork deductive); all forms of dogma, control, and domination—all impulses to completeness and certainty; and it asks us to appreciate the practical value of imperfection, serendipity, wildness. Completeness is a form of death; wildness is a form of fertility, growth.[13]

The open-ended nature of the universe explains why scientists continually discover new and unexpected properties of things. Properties continually evolve, self-organize, and emerge anew, as the law of emergent properties has discovered. Every time scientists feel they are closer to the ultimate answer, what they find instead is that there are more layers in which to investigate. For example, as particle physicists explore the heart of matter—the subatomic particle—they have found there is virtually no end to the limit of particles to be discovered. At last count hundreds of different particles have been found or postulated—with such names as pions, mesons, muons, leptons, neutrinos, quarks, antiquarks, tauans, tau neutrinos, gluons, baryons, neutralinos, wimps, champs, fermions, and bosons—some having life spans of 10 [-24] seconds. The physicist Enrico Fermi commented, "If I could remember the names of all these particles, I would have been a botanist."[14]

The comprehension of Godel's Theorem can allow for the expansion of linear determinism and with it the expansion of medical determinism. This comprehension is tantamount to a liberating experience, a freeing of the mind. That is why John Casti and Werner DePauli state that "understanding the logic underlying Godel's magnificent achievement has been described by some as akin to a religious or mystical experience."[15] And as Rucker states, "Paradoxically to understand Godel's proof is to find a sort of liberation. For many logic students, the final breakthrough to full understanding of the Incompleteness Theorem is practically a conversion experience. This is partly a by-product of the mystique Godel's name carries. But, more profoundly, to understand the essentially labyrinthine nature of the castle is, somehow, to be free of it."[16]

Understanding Godelian logic is seen as akin to a mystical or conversion experience because of the need to jump out of the system to solve the problem. In essence, one has to make a quantum leap in thinking. Cognitive science explains this as the jumping from a subsystem of one's brain to a wider subsystem.[17] It can also be explained using the concept of self-transcendence embraced by Zen and other eastern philosophies.

ZEN

Zen is considered a path towards liberation. It is an attempt to break through the obstructions that the mind sets through artificial conventions, and it gradually deepens one's self-awareness by gradually widening the scope of the system to which one adheres. Zen understands that the tendency of people is to dogmatize. As an eleventh century Song Dynasty Zen master explained:

> Zen teachers of true vision and great liberation have made changes in method along the way, to prevent people from sticking to names and forms and falling into rationalizations. Over the course of the centuries, Zen has branched out into different schools with individual methods, but the purpose is still the same—to point to the human mind. Once the ground of the mind is clarified, there is no obstruction. You shed views and interpretations based on concepts like victory and defeat, self and others, right and wrong. Thus you pass through all that and reach a realm of great rest and tranquility...All of these teachings are expedients, just for the purpose of breaking through obsessions, doubts, intellectual interpretations, and egocentric ideas.[18]

A Zen proverb states, "When one person transmits a falsehood, myriad people transmit it as truth."[19] Zen understands that it is necessary to break through the illusions that people hold in their mind as truths. But Zen does not advise a person to walk around in a transcendent state to achieve higher truths; Zen believes that the desire to attain transcendence will lead to a negative condition called "the annihilation of the self."[20] Instead, Zen's desire is for people to heighten both their rational and transrational capacities, in order to be able to have a heightened ability to discern and discriminate. By doing so, it is believed a person can achieve liberation of the mind and break through the dogmas and conventions by which one lives. Someone in such a state will then be living in a Godelian universe, in which that person will be able to grow, move from lesser to greater states of knowledge, and be capable of developing and evolving.

Zen would say the greatest fear people have is the liberation of the mind, of being afraid to expand one's parameters and widen one's worldview to the greatest extent possible. Others say the fear of the liberation of the mind is based on an innate fear of infinity, of being afraid of the vastness of space.

INFINITY

The sixteenth century philosopher, Giordano Bruno, was a strong advocate of the idea that the universe is infinite. The Church, outraged by his teachings, arrested him and demanded that he recant. He refused, so he was burned at the stake. A similar fate almost befell Galileo Galilei, the famed scientist who was a contemporary of Bruno. He was willing to recant, so instead of being burned alive, he was given a life sentence of house arrest. Galileo understood the problems comprehending infinity were due:

"When we attempt, with our finite minds, to discuss the infinite, assigning to it those properties which we give to the finite and limited; but this I think is wrong, for we cannot speak of infinite quantities as being the one greater or less than or equal to another."[21]

The nineteenth century mathematician, Georg Cantor, was the first to create a theory of infinity that proved its existence. "The fear of infinity is a form of myopia that destroys the possibility of seeing the actual infinite," he wrote, "even though it in its highest form has created and sustains us, and in its secondary transfinite forms occurs all around us and even inhabits our minds."[22]

Yet another perspective on infinity and our tenuous relationship to it comes not from another scientist, but from the noted Latin American essayist and short story author, Jorge Luis Borges. In his essay, "Avatars of the Tortoise," Borges wrote, "There is a concept which corrupts and upsets all others. I refer not to Evil, whose limited realm is that of ethics, I refer to the infinite."[23]

To grasp the enormity of the universe entails not a smashing of the worldview of scientism, but an expansion of it. Since this expanded worldview has shown itself to make scientific sense, a new scientific model will need to reflect this.

A NEW MEDICAL MODEL

The same might be said for medicine: a new medical model needs to be developed that expands the biomedical model and allows for a broader worldview, one that encompasses the various realms of life, from the biological to the psychological to the social and cultural. This is called the biopsychosocial model of medicine. It is not new, since it has been advocated for quite a long time by many different people.

The twelfth century physician, Moses Maimonides, wrote a book, the *Regimen Sanitatis*, or *The Preservation of Youth*, published in 1200, which embodied the essence of the biopsychosocial approach. In this book, Maimonides put forth that health was a composite process, encompassing the spiritual, natural, and physical. His belief was that each disease was unique and one disease was never like another, which led him to the conclusion that "a single remedy will not suffice to deal with all ailing bodies."[24] He advised the physician "to not treat the disease, but the patient who is suffering from it."[25]

The nineteenth century German pathologist, Rudolf Virchow (1821-1902), who was the founder of cell pathology, proclaimed that "medicine is a social science."[26] Because his work in cell pathology led him to understand the nature of diseased tissue, Virchow did not accept his colleague Louis Pasteur's germ theory of disease, which stated that the cause of all illness is germs. Instead Virchow believed that illness occurred for many reasons, with germs being just one of the possible causes. He felt that there was a relationship between illness and social and cultural issues. This belief developed from his many interests— besides being a pathologist, he was also an archaeologist and anthropologist, was involved in political and social issues, and was influential in German politics and served for a time in the German Reichstag.

A 1974 community mental health study of residents of New York City, the Midtown Manhattan Study, came to two conclusions about the relationship between social status and health and well-being. The study drew its conclusions based on the group being observed, and from a subgroup comprised only of the women from the overall group. Of the overall group, the study found that "improvements in a group's social status and role in a society's objective system of status allocations are conducive to improvements in that group's well-being and all other dimensions of health."[27] Regarding the women in the subgroup, the study concluded that there is "a cause-and-effect connection between the partial emancipation of women from their nineteenth century status of sexist servitude, and their twentieth century advances in subjective well-being."[28] This complemented the findings of Alice Hamilton (1869-1970), a pioneering physician of occupational medicine who worked with a mostly poor immigrant population in Chicago. Through her work experience, Hamilton came to understand that there was a connection between health, poverty, and social discrimination.[29]

It was George Engel, writing in the 1977 issue of *Science,* who proposed the word *biopsychosocial* as the new model of medicine, saying
that biomedicine was in crisis because it adhered to a model of disease
no longer adequate for the scientific tasks and social responsibilities of
medicine. Instead, he proposed a new model that would take account of
the patient as a person as well as of the illness.[30] Although the word was
new, the concept behind biopsychosocial medicine was not. In essence,
Engel was asking modern medicine to return to the days when the patient
was central to the physician's agenda.

Many diseases are now looked at through the lens of the biopsychosocial
model. These diseases include fibromyalgia;[31] irritable bowel syndrome;[32]
gastroesophageal reflux disease;[33] chronic pain;[34] and cancer.[35]

A biopsychosocial model of chronic diseases replaces reductionism with
a recognition of the complex causation of most diseases. The model also
recognizes the need for multiple approaches to healing. As such, it is a step
beyond the system and an expansion of medical determinism. However,
some say it is swinging the pendulum too far in the other direction, going
from a biomedical reductionism to a psychological reductionism. Larry
Dossey explains the seeming contradiction: "Starving persons tend to
overeat on being reintroduced to food. Deprived for so long of anything
remotely resembling the psychological or spiritual in health and illness,
now advocates selectively gorged on the 'psycho' aspect of the biopsychosocial models that began to emerge in the 1950s."[36]

In essence, some claim one type of reductionism is being replaced by
another type. As one physician laments, "We have reached the point
where patients and physicians alike dream up psychological components
in every pathology from cancer to hangnails…I think old-fashioned psychological reductionism is being cross-fertilized by the puritan American
version of the Protestant Ethic."[37]

Although a biopsychosocial model is an attempt to expand the parameters of biomedicine, it may still be tied into scientism by virtue of its
attempt to reduce things to a knowable and predictable quotient. This is
still linear determinism, although by a different name. No longer is illness seen as related to a cellular or molecular problem. The problem is
now seen differently: "We must search for health within ourselves. If we
don't have balance within ourselves, then we cannot expect the world to
stay in balance…we must begin within the borders of our own skin."[38] By

reducing all health concerns to a by-product of what is going on within the skin, there is a tendency to forget that a person is also a by-product of one's environment and connected to the larger whole.

What is needed, instead, is to take a truly Godelian approach—to see beyond medical and scientific determinism and view the workings of the world in a different and expanded light. To do so is to understand that this is a world that contains much indeterminacy and uncertainty.

Indeed, the process of healing has a spiritual and mysterious quality that transcends scientism. To get at the essence of this, create a new world-view and mental model, and transcend and truly jump out of the system, we need to incorporate this knowledge within the context of a broader scientific approach. In this broader perspective, the intersection between science and art and between rational thought and imagination begin to blend. As such, this is the entrance into the realm of the integral thinker. To enter into this domain, logic is not denied; rather, it is expanded in the broadest possible way, taking a person into a universe that operates by laws that both transcend and include the laws of scientism. This is a universe predicated on laws of quantum mechanics, complexity, and nonlinear dynamics; it is also a universe that has at its core a spiritual intelligence.

Chapter Notes:

1. Frege, quoted in Wang, Hao. "What is logic?" *The Monist*. 77, no. 3 (July 1994): 261.

2. Wittgenstein, quoted in Wang, "What is logic?" p. 262.

3. Godel, quoted in Wang, "What is logic?" p. 262.

4. Zebrowski, George. "Life in Godel's universe: Maps all the way." *Omni*. 14, no. 7 (April 1992): 54.

5. Casti, John L. and Werner DePauli. *Godel: A Life of Logic*. Cambridge, MA: Perseus Publishing, 2000: 20.

6. Michalko, Michael. *Cracking Creativity*. Berkeley: Ten Speed Press, 2001:5.

7. Rubik, Beverly. "Exploring the Frontiers of Science." Interview by Russell DiCarlo. *HealthWorld Online*, 1996: 9. www.healthy.net/asp/templates/interview.asp?PageType=Interview&ID=297.

8. Rucker, Rudy. *Infinity and the Mind*. Princeton: Princeton University Press, 1995: 165.

9. Von Neumann, in Zebrowski, "Life in Godel's universe: Maps all the way," p. 54.

10. Rucker, in Dossey, Larry. *Recovering the Soul: A Scientific and Spiritual Search*. New York: Bantam, 1989: 140.

11. Casti and DePauli, *Godel: A Life of Logic*, p. 3.

12. Hawking, Stephen. *The Universe in a Nutshell*. New York: Bantam, 2001.

13. Zebrowski, "Life in Godel's universe: Maps all the way," p. 56.

14. Fisher, Arthur. "The cosmic connection." *Popular Science*. 238, no. 4 (1991):72.

15. Casti and DePauli, *Godel: A Life of Logic*, p. 41.

16. Rucker, in Dossey, *Recovering the Soul: A Scientific and Spiritual Search*, p. 141.

17. Hofstadter, Douglas R. *Godel, Escher, Bach: An Eternal, Golden Braid*. New York: Vintage Books, 1979: 477.

18. Cleary, Thomas. *Zen Essence: The Science of Freedom*. Boston: Shambhala Publications, 1989: 27-28.

19. Cleary, Thomas. *Rational Zen: The Mind of Dogen Zenji*. Boston: Shambhala Publications, 1992: 16.

20. Suzuki, D. T. *Zen Buddhism*. Garden City, NY: Anchor Books, 1956: 14.

21. Galilei, Galileo. *Two New Sciences*. Translated by Henry Crew and Alfonso DeSalvio. New York: Macmillan: 26.

22. Cantor, Georg. *Gesammelte Abhandlugen*. Edited and translated by A. Fraenkel and E. Zermelo. Berlin: Springer-Verlag, 1932: 374.

23. Borges, Jorge Luis. "Avatars of the Tortoise." In *Labyrinths*. New York: New Directions, 1962: 202.

24. Maimonides, Moses. *The Medical Aphorisms of Moses Maimonides*. New York, Yeshiva University Press, 1970.

25. Bloch, Sidney. "Moses Maimonides' contribution to the biopsychosocial approach in clinical medicine." *Lancet*. 358, no. 9284 (Sept. 8, 2001): 829.

26. Virchow, quoted in Antonovsky, Aaron. "A sociological critique of the 'well-being' movement." *Advances: The Journal of Mind-Body Health*. 10, no. 3 (Summer 1994): 8.

27. Srole, L. and AK Fischer. "The Midtown Manhattan longitudinal study versus 'The mental paradise lost' doctrine." *Archives of General Psychiatry*. 37 (1980): 217.

28. Ibid.

29. Fee, Elizabeth and Theodore M. Brown. "Alice Hamilton: Settlement physician, occupational health pioneer." *American Journal of Public Health*. 91, no. 11 (Nov. 2001): 1767.

30. Engel, George L. "The need for a new medical model: The challenge for biomedicine." *Science*. 196, no. 4286 (April 8, 1977): 131.

31. Littlejohn, GO and J. Walker. "A realistic approach to managing patients with fibromyalgia." *Current Rheumatology Reports*. 4, no. 4 (August 2002): 286-92.

32. Ringel, Y and DA Drossman. "Irritable bowel syndrome: Classification and conceptualization." *Journal of Clinical Gastroenterology*. 35, no. 1 Supplement (July, 2002): S7-S10.

33. Kamolz, T and V. Velanovich. "Psychological and emotional aspects of gastroesophageal reflux disease." Diseases of the Esophagus: *The Official Journal of the International Society for Diseases of the Esophagus*. 15, no. 3 (2002): 199-203.

34. Nielson, WR and R. Weir. "Biopsychosocial approaches to the treatment of pain." *Clinical Journal of Pain*. 17, no. 4 Supplement (Dec. 2001): S114-27.

35. Temoshok, Lydia. "We need to study the psychosocial impact of medical interventions." *Advances: The Journal of Mind-Body Health*. 13, no. 1 (Winter 1997): 51-53.

36. Dossey, Larry. "Antonovsky's perspective may not go far enough." *Advances: The Journal of Mind-Body Health*. 10, no. 3 (Summer 1994): 13.

37. Levenstein, Susan. "Wellness, health, Antonovsky." *Advances: The Journal of Mind-Body Health*. 10, no. 3 (Summer 1994): 28.

38. Antonovsky, "A sociological critique of the 'well-being' movement," p. 7.

Five

Quantum Laws

The universe appears to be a far different place than what was mapped out during the Scientific Revolution in the seventeenth century when the worldview promulgated was that of scientism, or scientific materialism. Isaac Newton's (1642-1727) complete mathematical formulation of the mechanistic view of nature was the highest expression of that worldview. His work was such a crowning achievement that Einstein called it "perhaps the greatest advance in thought that a single individual was ever privileged to make."[1]

NEWTON'S VISION

By building on the work of Galileo and Descartes, Newton invented differential calculus, which allowed him to describe the motion of solid bodies and to formulate the general laws of motion governing all objects in the solar system. His vision was of a clockwork universe in which the entire universe ran smoothly like a precision clock and was governed by immutable laws. He viewed matter as "solid, massy impenetrable, movable particles."[2] Newton wrote, "Absolute space, in its own nature, without regard to anything external, remains always similar and immovable...Absolute, true, and mathematical time, of itself and by its own nature, flows uniformly, without regard to anything external."[3]

In this clockwork universe life was seen as completely predictable, with all outcomes capable of being determined and known. Everything in the universe was viewed in this deterministic manner: force fields usher matter along known paths, leading to an outcome that can always be predicted.

Interestingly, Newton dabbled in alchemy and metaphysics.[4] "He was the last of the magicians," wrote John Maynard Keynes, "the last of the Babylonians and Sumerians, the last great mind which looked out on the visible and intellectual world with the same eyes as those who began to build our intellectual inheritance rather less than 10,000 years ago."[5]

Newton's interest in alchemy was reflected in his vision of a universe made up of hard, indivisible particles constantly acted upon by a system of various non-material attractive and repulsive forces.[6] To the dismay of some of his scientific contemporaries, Newton invoked this alchemical notion of hidden and unknown forces of attraction and repulsion between bodies, against the straightforward mechanistic notion of force via impact.[7]

Yet, it was not this quasi-mystical approach that Newton's colleagues and future scientists adopted; rather, it was the deterministic model to which they pledged their allegiance. The eighteenth century mathematician Pierre-Simon de Laplace summed up the philosophical importance of the deterministic approach:

> An intelligence that, at a given instant, could comprehend all the forces by which nature is animated and the respective situation of the beings that make it up, if moreover it were vast enough to submit these data to analysis, would encompass in the same formula the movements of the greatest bodies of the universe and those of the lightest atoms. For such an intelligence nothing would be uncertain, and the future, like the past, would be open to its eyes.[8]

The adherence to a deterministic perspective led to a rigid lock-step view of the unfolding of the entire universe. Everything was seen as capable of predictability in the past, present, and future.

However, there was a problem with Newton's most famous discovery—the theory of gravity—and this problem was the chink in the armor of determinism. Because his interests in alchemy and the occult had informed Newton's conceptual thinking, he had basically made a visionary leap of faith with his theory of gravity. He surmised that an invisible force, or an invisible mechanism, existed in nature and operates across great distances. He envisioned the entire universe as a system interconnected by the force of gravity. Moreover, his vision of gravity fit his spiritual/mystical vision of God; gravity was an expression of an invisible force that connected the universe as a whole.[9]

Newton himself was well aware of the problem and addressed it directly:

> It is inconceivable, that inanimate brute matter, should, without the mediation of something else, which is not material, operate upon and affect other matter without mutual contact. That Gravity should be innate, inherent and essential to matter so that one body may act upon another at a distance thro' a vacuum without the mediation of anything else, by and through which their action and force may be conveyed, from one to another, is to me so great an absurdity that I believe no Man who has in philosophical matters a competent faculty of thinking can ever fall into it. Gravity must be caused by an agent acting constantly according to certain laws; but whether this agent be material or immaterial, I have left consideration of my readers.[10]

Newton was able to prove the existence of gravity, but he never was able to give insight into how it worked. The best he could conjecture was that gravity was a field that traveled via the vehicle of light, and he conjectured that light, like everything else in the universe, consisted of a stream of tiny particles. A contemporary of Newton, the Dutch physicist Christiaan Huygens (1629-1695), proposed an alternative theory that light was a wave. Since the entire universe was considered to be made of material particles, Huygens proposed that the light waves traveled through the universe via an invisible, yet material, substance called the "luminiferous ether."[11] Although the two contrasting theories about the nature of light competed for the spotlight over the next few hundred years, the concept of the ether as the vehicle for carrying light became an accepted scientific truth.

By the nineteenth century light and radio waves were established as electromagnetic wavelike phenomena, traveling through empty space in the material medium known as the ether. In 1887 physicists Albert Michelson and Edward Morley set out, once and for all, to prove the existence of the ether, which up to that point, had been purely an accepted hypothesis.

According to classical/Newtonian theory, the ether would have to fill all of space, including the empty vacuum of space, and evince the stiffness of a material much stiffer than steel. Michelson and Morley were convinced that something with these remarkable properties could be detected if an appropriate experiment could be conducted. Unfortunately, the experiment they devised to prove the existence of the ether failed, leaving both scientists terribly disappointed with their efforts.[12]

Physicists came up with new theories, some bordering on preposterous, to explain away the failure of the Michelson-Morley experiment. In doing so, they refused to accept the conclusions of the experiment that questioned the existence of the ether. One of the most prominent physicists of the late nineteenth century, Lord Kelvin (nee William Thomson), said a few years after the Michelson-Morley experiment, "One thing we are sure of, and that is the reality and substantiality of the luminiferous ether."[13] Since no one had an alternative explanation, an explanation that would have run smack in the face of everything that Newton had delineated, the status quo was maintained, regardless of its implausibility.

In the next section, I will be discussing the theories of Albert Einstein and what made his concepts so special. In the section after, I will discuss quantum theory, which Einstein helped uncover. Both discussions will be somewhat scientific and technical. Because it is an important part of the story, I feel it has to be told in the proper context. For those who find these discussions somewhat hard to follow, I recommend you skim through these two sections and begin again in the last section of this chapter, Nonlocality.

Albert Einstein's Vision

Things began to change in 1905 when Albert Einstein (1879-1955), then a patent clerk in Bern, Switzerland, put forth his Special Theory of Relativity and then in 1916 proposed his General Theory of Relativity. Expounding on Newton's theories and incorporating the work of other physicists of the time, such as Max Planck (who was also starting to explain the workings of the universe in a new light), Einstein broke new ground and helped radically change our notions of space and time, and matter and energy. Besides putting forward the two Relativity theories, Einstein also wrote a series of papers in support of his doctoral thesis, which paved the way for other new understandings, including quantum theory.[14, 15, 16]

His special theory of relativity was a new conceptualization of material objects, motion, and light that showed that space and time are not separate dimensions but are interrelated. In this theory, space and time are both aspects of a larger whole—space-time—and their mass and energy can be interconverted to a limited extent.[17] Space and time were also found to be relative concepts, different for every observer. Thus, two observers in relative motion measuring the positions and times of the same events would get different results. At the same time, certain quantities of the universe are absolute—the speed of light is one and the space-time interval is another.[18] Based on his law, Einstein was able to prove that the ether was a myth. That did not negate that light traveled through space. Instead, it showed that it did not travel through a medium such as an ether. Einstein demonstrated in his Theory of Special Relativity and in one of the other papers he wrote in 1905 that light waves, along with particles, are equally fundamental.[19]

In his Theory of General Relativity, Einstein saw gravity not as a force that occurs between massive bodies, but as the influence of those bodies on the entirety of space-time. He proposed an interaction between mass-energy and the structure of space-time, creating curvatures in space, thereby countering a Euclidean geometrical version of reality. In Euclidean geometry the universe is seen as being in a perfect grid, shaped in a logically deterministic manner. Einstein's theory showed that gravity is not a force, but a curvature in space-time and that objects that are falling move in straight lines subject to the standards of gravity.[20,21,22]

By virtue of his Theory of General Relativity, Einstein proved that all mass and energy warp space and time so that bodies tend to fall together. Einstein's theories transformed the understanding of the universe from one in which space and time were seen as passive spectators to one in which they were active participants in the dynamics of the cosmos.[23]

As revolutionary as Einstein's vision of the universe was, most of it was built on Newton's theories and completed them, as opposed to destroying them. One of his other papers written in 1905, for which he won a Nobel Prize in 1921, radically altered Newton's theories. The paper concerned the photoelectric effect and suggested that light is composed not of continuous waves but of particles, called photons, whose energy is proportional to the frequency of the light radiation.[24] Recognized as the first scientific work dealing with what is now called quantum mechanics, it expanded on theories first put forth by the German physicist Max Planck (1858-1947) in 1900.

At the end of the nineteenth century, all the big problems in physics had been considered solved, giving physicists what they thought was a comprehensive picture of the way the world worked. In fact, Max Planck, whose discoveries inspired Einstein to explore further, was discouraged from going into physics by his teacher. "Physics is finished, young man," he told Planck. "It's a dead-end street." He suggested Planck become a concert pianist.[25] Fortunately, Planck didn't heed his teacher's advice. Instead, he discovered an entire new picture of the world.

The Quantum Vision

Planck put forth the hypothesis that energy, like matter, is composed of tiny bundles or packets of particles, which he named quanta. He considered the quanta to be the smallest discrete amount of matter in the microscopic world. He suggested that a quanta's energy is proportional to the frequency of its radiation and is emitted or absorbed not in smooth, continuous movements, but in specific, discontinuously discrete amounts. Einstein expanded on Planck's hypothesis by stating that light is a quanta, and it is also emitted or absorbed in discontinuous and discrete amounts. Thus began the field of quantum mechanics, a field that contradicted Newton's concept of a deterministic universe, instead showing a universe, as one physicist called it, of "lumps and jumps."[26] In other words, instead of moving in predictable, continuous movements, matter and energy move in fits and starts.

Einstein's 1905 paper on the photoelectric effect opened up a whole new arena for investigation, one that was carried out on many fronts and by many people, each making important contributions to the field, men such as Planck, Einstein, Paul Dirac (1902-1984), Erwin Schroedinger (1887-1961), Niels Bohr (1885-1962), and Werner Heisenberg (1901-1976).

Quantum mechanics does not have one founder because it was an evolution of thought by a number of men, sometimes working collegially, sometimes working contentiously. At first, these pioneers who pressed forward with their discoveries were not totally sure where they were going. All they knew was that they were mapping out a model quite unlike any that had been known before. A French physicist, Oliver Costa de Beauregard, called the 1900-1925 period the "Quantum Stone Age" because the physicists working on quantum theory didn't yet have a coherent theory but instead were putting things together piecemeal.[27]

By 1925 the first coherent quantum theory was born. Actually in that year, three quantum theories independently arose. Heisenberg was first in the summer of 1925, when he announced his theory of matrix mechanics. Later that year, two more theories were declared. Schroedinger demonstrated his theory of wave mechanics, and Dirac explained his transformation theory. All three theories turned out to be correct, using different perspectives to reach the same conclusions.[28] These theories allowed for the coalescing of ideas, and the spawning of even more new discoveries.

According to the theories, matter was both particle and wave, but its movement or location could only be predicted, and not known for certain, because there was too much uncertainty in the movement of these particle/waves. Instead, it was found that the only thing that can be predicted about matter is that it has tendencies to exist. The theory postulated that matter can be both particle and wave simultaneously and it was only in the act of observation or measurement that it became one or the other. Niels Bohr considered the ability for matter to have this dual role to be a fundamental aspect of nature: matter can be both something tangible, when it is a particle, and something intangible, when it is a wave.

The dual role that matter plays came to be known as the Principle of Complementarity, which stated that at its fundamental level matter has a dual nature both as wave and particle. To describe it as one or the other is not a true and complete description of reality. Rather, wave and particle are considered to have a complementary and dualistic relationship. According to quantum theory, the complementary nature of matter is the essential nature of all things. Physicist William Bragg stated the duality well when he said, "Elementary particles seem to be waves on Mondays, Wednesdays, and Fridays, and particles on Tuesdays, Thursdays, and Saturdays."[29]

This new and radical view of the universe broke down the division between observer and observed, and object and subject, and instead saw an interplay between the two and an interconnectedness between all objects. As physicist Henry Stapp put it, "Each atom turns out to be nothing but the potentialities in the behavior pattern of others. What we find, therefore, are not elementary space-time realities, but rather a web of relationships in which no part can stand alone; every part derives its meaning and existence only from its place within the whole."[30]

Einstein had difficulty with the universe as sketched out by quantum theory. He and Bohr had a series of public debates on the subject over the years. At one debate Heisenberg recalled, "In the morning, Einstein presents a challenge designed to prove the inadequacy of quantum theory. And every evening, after a day of hard thought, Bohr would have found some flaw in Einstein's reasoning."[31] Einstein would say such things as, "Quantum mechanics is very worthy of regard, but an inner voice tells me that this is not the true Jacob. The theory yields a lot, but it hardly brings us any closer to the secret than the old one. In any case, I am convinced that He doesn't throw dice."[32] Bohr would then counter, "It's not our business to prescribe to God how He should run the world."[33]

Experiment after experiment has proven quantum mechanics to be a true theory and Einstein to be wrong. As Stephen Hawking has written, "Einstein was confused, not quantum theory."[34]

If Einstein was confused, it is understandable because the findings that have resulted from quantum theory have been mind-boggling. Niels Bohr alluded to this himself when he said, "Anyone who is not shocked by quantum theory has not understood it."[35] The physicist Richard Feynman (1918-1988) has said:

> There was a time when the newspapers said that only twelve men understood the theory of relativity. I do not believe there ever was such a time. There might have been a time when only one man did because he was the only guy who caught on, before he wrote his paper. But after people read the paper a lot of people understood the theory of relativity in one way or other, certainly more than twelve. On the other hand I think I can safely say that nobody understands quantum mechanics.[36]

The reason that nobody understands quantum mechanics, according to Feynman, is that it gives a very different picture of the way nature operates. Heisenberg remembers "discussions with Bohr which went through many hours till very late at night and ended almost in despair, and when at the end of the discussion I went alone for a walk in the neighboring park I repeated to myself again and again the question: 'Can nature possibly be as absurd as it seemed to us in these atomic experiments?'"[37]

Quantum theory claims that nature does not fully operate the way Newton envisioned it. To comprehend it requires people to adjust their mental models of how they view the universe. Quantum theory shows that the universe is not deterministic, but rather highly probabilistic and uncertain. Matter in the form of waves originates from a quantum vacuum, a gigantic vacuum teeming with an infinite amount of information and energy that pervades the entire universe. The quantum vacuum is thought to be the source of the Big Bang and the origins of the universe. It is potentially a wonderland of effects: force fields that emerge from nowhere, particles popping in and out of existence, and energetic jitterings with no apparent power source. Some scientists even contemplate the prospect of harnessing the vacuum's properties to provide a limitless supply of energy.[38]

Once matter waves emanate from the quantum vacuum, they can potentially spread out infinitely in their quantum state, across the universe in all directions. This was what Heisenberg called matrix mechanics, and Schroedinger considered wave mechanics, or the wave function; Feynman called it the sum over histories.[39] Adopting the quantum cosmological view, Stephen Hawking states that a system does not have just a single history in space-time, but rather has every possible history.[40]

The possibility of a system having every possible history led to the "many worlds" version of quantum theory first put forth by Hugh Everett in 1957. Although it sounds close to science fiction, many reputable scientists believe this "many worlds" theory to be true. In this scenario, if a particle appears to be occupying many positions at once, that is because it does. Everett believed that all quantum states are equally real and that if we see only one state, other versions must exist elsewhere where they are seen by others.[41]

NONLOCALITY

Although Einstein stated that the speed of light is an absolute quantity for all entities, quantum physicists also have called this into question. Einstein's theory is based on a local universe, in which all material objects must travel through space one bit at a time with a finite velocity.[42] Quantum theory hypothesizes just the opposite, that there is a nonlocal aspect to the universe. Two quantum objects can come together, divide, and then travel on separate and distinct paths through the universe, all the while maintaining a connection with each other. Einstein again vehemently disagreed, not believing in what he called "spooky action-at-a-distance."[43] However, Irish physicist John Bell showed, in an experiment in 1964 that has been repeated and proven by other physicists many times since, that the universe is nonlocal and that there is a quantum interconnectedness that travels faster than light. Bell said about his findings, " My theorem answers some of Einstein's questions in a way that Einstein would have liked the least."[44]

Heisenberg understood the implications of quantum theory many decades earlier when he stated that the cosmos appears to be "a complicated tissue of events, in which connections of different kinds alternate or overlay or combine and thereby determine the texture of the whole."[45] Some observers believe that what lies at the foundation of the universe and creates these "connections of different kinds" is something that a deterministic universe cannot account for—information. In the quantum state a communication takes place via frequencies and signals that are not relayed by conventional energy transfer but by information transfer.[46] Many believe the vehicle for information transfer is consciousness.

Chapter Notes

1. Einstein, quoted in Capra, Fritjof. *The Tao of Physics*. Berkeley: Shambhala Publications, 1975: 56.

2. Davies, Paul and John Gribbin. *The Matter Myth*. New York: Simon and Schuster, 1992: 11.

3. Newton, quoted in Capra, *The Tao of Physics*, p. 55.

4. Harris, Paul L. "The last of the magicians? Children, scientists, and the invocation of hidden causal powers." *Child Development*. 68, no. 6 (Dec. 1997): 1019.

5. Keynes, John Maynard. *Essays in Biography*. London: Macmillan, 1951: 363.

6. Koyre, Alexandre. *From the Closed World to the Infinite Universe*. Baltimore: John Hopkins University Press, 1957: 207.

7. Henry, J. "Magic and science in the sixteenth and seventeenth centuries." In R.C. Olby, G.N. Cantor, J.R.R. Christie and M.J.S. Hodge (eds.). *Companion to the History of Science*. London: Routledge, 1990: 583-96.

8. De Laplace, Pierre-Simon. *Philosophical Essays on Probabilities*. Translated by Andrew I. Dale. New York: Springer-Verlag, 1995.

9. Westfall, Robert. *Never at Rest: A Biography of Isaac Newton*. Cambridge, England: Cambridge University Press, 1980.

10. Newton, Isaac. *Sir Isaac Newton's Mathematical Principle of Natural Philosophy and His System of the World*. Translated by A. Motte and Florian Cajori. Berkeley: University of California Press, 1962: 634.

11. Gribbin, John. *In Search of Schroedinger's Cat.* New York: Bantam, 1984: 10.

12. Nadeau, Robert, and Menas Kafatos. *The Non-Local Universe*. New York: Oxford University Press, 1999: 19.

13. Kelvin, quoted in Herbert, Nick. *Quantum Reality*. New York: Anchor Books, 1985: 7.

14. Gribbin, *In Search of Schroedinger's Cat*.

15. Herbert, *Quantum Reality*.

16. Greene, Brian. *The Elegant Universe*. New York: W. W. Norton & Company, 1999.

17. Zohar, Danah. *Who's Afraid of Schroedinger's Cat?* New York: Quill /William Morrow, 1997: 319.

18. Herbert, *Quantum Reality*, p. 7.

19. Ibid, pp. 47-49.

20. Gribbin, *In Search of Schroedinger's Cat*.

21. Herbert, *Quantum Reality*.

22. Nadeau and Kafatos, *The Non-Local Universe*.

23. Hawking, Stephen. "A brief history of relativity." *Time*. 154, no. 27 (Dec. 31, 1999): 79.

24. Rohmann, Chris. *A World of Ideas*. New York: Ballantine Books, 1999: 110.

25. Herbert, *Quantum Reality*, p. 31.

26. Zohar, *Who's Afraid of Schroedinger's Cat?* p. 296.

27. Herbert, *Quantum Reality*, p. 40.

28. Ibid, pp. 42-43.

29. Bragg, in Koestler, Arthur. *The Roots of Coincidence*. London: Hutchinson, 1972: 52.

30. Stapp, Stapp, Henry P. "Quantum physics and the physicist's view of nature: philosophical implications of Bell's theorem." In Richard E. Kitchener (ed.). *The World View of Contemporary Physics*. Albany, NY: S.U.N.Y. Press, 1988: 54.

31. Heisenberg, quoted in Flowers, Charles. *A Science Odyssey: One Hundred Years of Discovery*. New York: William Morrow, 1998: 32.

32. Einstein, quoted in *Flowers, A Science Odyssey: One Hundred Years of Discovery*, p. 32.

33. Bohr, quoted in *Flowers, A Science Odyssey: One Hundred Years of Discovery*, p. 32.

34. Hawking, quoted in *Greene, The Elegant Universe*, p. 108.

35. Gribbin, *In Search of Schroedinger's Cat*, p. 5.

36. Feynman, Richard. *The Character of Physical Law*. Cambridge, MA: MIT Press, 1965: 129.

37. Heisenberg, quoted in Herbert, *Quantum Reality*, p. 55.

38. Matthews, Robert. "Nothing like a vacuum." *New Scientist*. 145, no. 1966 (Feb. 25, 1995): 31.

39. Herbert, *Quantum Reality*.

40. Hawking, Stephen. *Black Holes and Baby Universes*. New York: Bantam, 1993:79.

41. Folger, Tim. "Quantum shmantum." *Discover*. 22, no. 9 (Sept. 2001): 40.

42. Goswami, Amit. *The Self-Aware Universe: How Consciousness Creates the Material World*. New York: Jeremy P. Tarcher/Putnam, 1993: 17.

43. Lindley, David. *Where Does the Weirdness Go?* New York: BasicBooks, 1996: 8.

44. Herbert, Nick. *Consciousness and Quantum Reality*. Interview by Jeffrey Mishlove. Thinking Allowed Productions, 1998: 4. www.intuition.org/txt/herbert.htm.

45. Heisenberg, Werner. *Physics and Philosophy*. London: Faber, 1959: 96.

46. Ho, Mae-Wan. "Toward an Indigenous Western Science: Causality in the Universe of Coherent Space-Time Structures." In Jane Clark and Willis Harman (eds.). *New Metaphysical Foundations of Modern Science*. Sausalito, CA: Institute of Noetic Sciences, 1994: 196-98.

Six

Quantum Laws, Consciousness, and Medicine

CONSCIOUSNESS AND NONLOCALITY

The possibility of consciousness playing a role in the workings of the universe is something the early quantum physicists considered. Their findings led them to remark that the universe is a far different place than the legacy of Descartes, Bacon, Newton and others had led them to believe.

Here are several examples. James Jeans stated, "The concepts which now prove to be fundamental to our understanding of nature...seem to my mind to be structures of pure thought...the universe begins to look more like a great thought than like a great machine."[1] Bohr commented, "The impossibility of distinguishing in our customary way between physical phenomena and their observation places us, in a position quite similar to that which is so familiar in psychology where we are continually reminded of the difficulty of distinguishing between subject and object."[2] The physicist Arthur Eddington said: "The stuff of the world is mind-stuff...The mind-stuff is not spread in space and time...Recognizing that the physical world is entirely abstract and without 'actuality' apart from its linkage to consciousness, we restore consciousness to the fundamental position."[3]

Today, scientist John Archibald Wheeler is the elder statesman of quantum physics. Born in 1911, he was a colleague of Einstein and Bohr, and has become a mentor to many of today's leading physicists. He is devoting what he considers his final years to one question: "How come existence?"[4] For Wheeler people are not simply bystanders on a cosmic stage; they are shapers and creators living in a participatory universe. He has created an experiment that he believes proves his conjecture that the universe is an enormous feedback loop, in which people contribute to the ongoing creation of not just the present and the future, but the past as well.[5]

Wheeler's investigation, which he calls his "delayed-choice experiment" is a hypothetical experiment, what is known as a "thought experiment" that he feels proves his hypothesis that the present can affect the past. In his experiment Wheeler suggests that a photon emitted from a distant quasar billions of light-years from Earth can simultaneously follow two paths to Earth, and observations made by astronomers today can then decide which path the photon took billions of years ago. In 1984, physicists at the University of Maryland, using a tabletop version of the delayed choice experiment, were able to demonstrate this effect. Wheeler believes this proof shows that the past and future are both still undetermined. He also believes that by peering back into time, present observations select one of many possible quantum histories for the entire universe.[6]

Stanford physicist Andre Lind agrees with Wheeler's view, believing that conscious observers are an essential component of the universe.

> The universe and the observer exist as a pair. You can say that the universe is there only when there is an observer who can say "Yes, I see the universe there." These small words—it looks like it was here—for practical purposes, it may not matter much, but for me as a human being, I do not know any sense in which I could claim that the universe is here in the absence of observers. We are together, the universe and us. The moment you say that the universe exists without any observers, I cannot make any sense out of that. I cannot imagine a consistent theory of everything that ignores consciousness.[7]

The concept of a consciousness that extends far beyond the reaches of a local mind is anomalous to scientific materialism. Yet, it fits in with a Godelian version of an open-ended universe, and it also fits in with a quantum vision of reality. So-called anomalies are not so much demonstrations of shortfalls in knowledge as much as indicators of the inadequacy of the present-day scientific approach and the mental models that uphold it.

If the concept of infinity is integrated with the knowledge of an open-ended universe, the entire notion of space-time may need to be revised, as is currently being done in some branches of physics. It is now hypothesized that there are many extra dimensions beyond Einstein's four dimensions; there may be as many as 10, 26, 96, 192, or it may be possible that the universe is infinite-dimensional. Standard space-time is being shown to be a subspace of a much higher dimensional space.[8]

In this multi-dimensional space, also known as hyperspace, it is thought that hyperspace is consciousness acting on itself. Eddington and other physicists think that the structure that physics discovers is the ultimate structure of the human mind.[9] Just as four dimensional space-time is part of hyperspace, the human mind is considered to be a small part of a much greater mind.[10] According to this view, the mind is a quantum system capable of spreading out infinitely across the universe and interacting in a participatory way with the universe.

However, people are capable of being in only one place at one time; no one has a mind that physically reaches out from their body into the infinite universe. Physicist Nick Herbert playfully touched on this theme with his song, "Bell's Theorem Blues":

> Doctor Bell say we connected
> He call me on the phone
> Doctor Bell say we united
> He call me on the phone
> But if we really together baby
> How come I feel so all alone[11]

Herbert clarifies the meaning of his song by stating:

> Yes, we're all connected in a sense, but in another sense we're not connected. There's a certain balance in nature. All the patterns are perfectly ordinary; they preserve space and time, and they're separated at light speed. Yet the bricks that make up these patterns are not that way at all. They don't know anything about space and time, and

> they're connected instantaneously...What Bell proved
> was that no model of the world that used only local con-
> nections would work. Everything is nonlocal.[12]

What Herbert is saying is that there is a balance between the quantum world and the everyday world. While things obey certain absolutes and there are certain constraints within a local universe, there is always the possibility they will not obey the constraints. Hence, systems can behave nonlocally. In other words, there is much indeterminacy in the world, and a science that reflects this gives a much truer picture of reality.

If science expanded its worldview to reflect this, medicine, as a field of science, would have to follow suit. A nonlocal aspect to medicine would have to be given more credence, in line with the awareness that the nonlocal aspect of mind and reality is a proven fact. The meaning of a nonlocal mind is a consciousness that is nonlocal, infinite in space and time, has no boundaries, and can extend from local mind to the infinite depths of the universe.

The CIA spent over 20 years investigating the potential of nonlocal consciousness under the aegis of remote, distant viewing, which is viewing which is not limited by space and time. They set up the Stanford Research Institute (SRI) in Menlo Park, California, headed by physicist Russell Targ, to investigate this potential. Since this was during the Cold War when the CIA was interested in getting a competitive edge on the Soviet Union, they were primarily interested in seeing if it was possible for people to use remote viewing to see into the USSR's top secret facilities and other highly classified areas.

The CIA has only recently declassified some of its files on its remote viewing experiments, but enough had been made public to allow Targ to co-author a book about it, called *Miracles of Mind* (1998). In the book Targ reports on the thousands of successful experiments that were conducted. When Targ and his colleagues reported their findings to the Congressional House Committee on Intelligence Oversight, Congressman Charles Rose stated, "What these people 'saw' was confirmed by aerial photography. There is no way it could have been faked."[13]

NONLOCAL MEDICINE

Physician Larry Dossey, who is a strong advocate for a nonlocal medicine, believes the field of medicine is undergoing a revolution. He has mapped out what he considers to be three eras of medicine: Era I—physical medicine; Era II—mind-body medicine; and Era III—nonlocal medicine. He considers Eras I and II to be local medicine, while he considers Era III nonlocal medicine. He describes the eras in the following way:

Era I—Mechanical, material, or physical medicine

It is causal and deterministic, and describable by classical concepts of space-time and matter-energy. Mind is not a factor; mind is a result of brain mechanisms. Examples of it are any form of therapy focusing solely on effects of things in the body, such as drugs, surgery, irradiation, CPR, etc.

Era II—Mind-Body Medicine

Mind is a major factor in healing within the single person; mind has causal powers. Medicine is thus not fully explainable by classical concepts in physics. Era II includes but goes beyond Era I. Examples are any therapy emphasizing the effects of consciousness solely with the individual body: psychoneuroimmunology, counseling, hypnosis, biofeedback, relaxation therapies, and most of imagery-based alternative therapies.

Era III—Nonlocal Medicine

Mind is a factor in healing both within and between persons. Mind is not completely localized to points in space (brains or bodies) or time (present moment or single life-times). Mind is unbounded in space and time and thus is ultimately unitary or one. Healing at a distance is possible. It is not describable by classical concepts of space-time and matter-energy. Examples of this are any therapy in which the effects of consciousness bridge between different persons: all forms of distant healing, intercessory prayer, and transpersonal imagery.[14]

There are many written cases of healings in the scientific literature,[15] as well as a large and growing number of anecdotal reports, which do not fit within the worldview of scientism. They do fit within the worldview of a nonlocal medicine, what Larry Dossey calls Era III medicine, a medicine that taps into something beyond the laws of a local universe, in which it is possible for healing to occur at a distance. There have also been two major studies showing the efficacy of nonlocal medicine: one studied distance healing, and the other studied prayer[16,17]. There have also been more than 130 other controlled trials performed that have documented the healing benefits of nonlocal medicine. Some of these were conducted on enzymes, cells, yeast, bacteria, plants, and animals in order to dispel the notion that any sort of placebo effect was occurring.[18]

In fact, the placebo effect may even be a nonlocal healing phenomenon and may be a demonstration of the power of the mind to effect a healing result. Studies of the placebo effect have often showed intriguing results. There have been fake surgeries in which people who believed they had surgery felt as well post-"surgery" as the surgical group.[19] People with asthma who were given a placebo solution they were told had an allergen in it saw a worsening of their asthma. When they were given an inhaler with the same placebo solution and told the inhaler had a medicine in it to help asthma, their airways opened up.[20]

The list of placebo studies is quite long. What the body of evidence points to is that the greatest healing source of all may be the power of the mind. Perhaps the mind's ability to create placebo effects is based on its ability to tap into something beyond itself, something nonlocal, something part of the greater universe, and part of the quantum vacuum.

What these experiments and studies imply is that there is a great healing force within the body, and this force has a spiritual dimension. Many traditional healers believe that medicine is primarily spiritual. "Healing is 80% spiritual and 20% medicine," says Papa Henry Auwae, a 96-year-old po'okela, or master of Hawaiian herbal medicine.[21] A practitioner of traditional Arabic medicine, Ali Pul, believes that "the medicine of the soul is the medicine of the body."[22]

The National Center for Complementary and Alternative Medicine (NCCAM) is one of a number of Centers within the National Institutes of Health. It plays an advocacy role in the field of Complementary Medicine, funding research into various aspects of the field. Some of the research funded includes specific clinical trials, examining the role of a specific agent or intervention in the treatment of a specific ailment. Other studies are broader in scope and concept. One project title currently under review by the NCCAM that fits into this broader category involves the concept of nonlocal medicine. The project is officially called the "Frontier Medicine Program." Its description states that Frontier Medicine "can be defined, for purposes of this program, as those complementary and alternative medicine (CAM) practices for which there is no plausible biomedical explanation. Examples include bioelectromagnetic therapy, energy healing, homeopathy, and therapeutic prayer."[23]

In addition to the Frontier Medicine program, the NCCAM has also been funding other studies that explore the realm of nonlocal medicine. These studies have such titles as:

> Holistic Health: Healing from the Inside
> Healing and Expectation: CAM patient-healer interactions
> Spirituality and Will to Live in Patients with HIV/AIDS
> Distant Healing Efforts for AIDS by nurses and "healers"
> Efficacy of Distant Healing in Glioblastoma Treatment[24]

The NCCAM is only one among many institutions conducting research into nonlocal healing mechanisms. Other prestigious institutions conducting research include McGill University; the University of California, San Francisco, Medical School; New England Deaconness Hospital; Duke University Medical Center; and the Geraldine Brush Cancer Research Institute.[25]

FRONTIER SCIENCE

Just as biomedicine is a component of science, frontier medicine might be said to be a component of frontier science. As with frontier medicine, there are a number of research units around the world affiliated with universities that are studying frontier science.[26] Biophysicist Beverly Rubik, one of the best known advocates of frontier science, defines it as, "Science that is outside of the mainstream but has a significant numbers of scholars asking questions within its domain. Topics such as consciousness studies and the science underlying alternative medicine are examples of what I call frontier science."[27]

Rubik states that one of the mechanisms fundamental to frontier science is nonlocality and its relationship to mind and consciousness:

> We talk about mind in frontier physics as if it were a nonlocal phenomenon, a la Bell's Theorem. In other words, in the quantum world everything is fundamentally interconnected. And mind has this property that when intention is applied it can be highly specific toward another person, even on the other side of the planet, and effects can be seen. We really don't fundamentally understand consciousness, but we can make an analogy to the world of quantum mechanics since we see evidence of this nonlocality in the realm of particles. In other words, if particles were once connected and later become separated from each other, they remain correlated even if they're on opposite ends of the universe. Humans apparently have the same kind of holistic interconnectedness that remains. We don't understand consciousness, but we can invoke the possibility of nonlocality from quantum physics. Perhaps it is how prayer and intention to heal work successfully over long distance. Again, these phenomena are not fully explained by science as we know it. I would say the experimental evidence is certainly strong, but our theories are weak.[28]

Rubik is involved in many studies that seek to produce a body of experimental evidence pointing to the validity of a nonlocal consciousness. In one experiment she explored two cultures of single-celled algae that glow. She found that when one of them was disturbed with a chemical stressor, it emitted a burst of light. Almost simultaneously the second culture that was in a separate container also emitted light, as if it was communicating with the first culture.[29]

In another experiment which she did with a German colleague, they found that the body and all organisms emit a low-level light, and they were able to measure it using very sensitive detectors that counts photons, the particles of light coming out of the body. By doing this they showed that the light is coherent, like a laser. What they believe this demonstrates is that the emitted light carries information and may be involved in an internal, as well as external, communication system that conveys signals between living things.[30]

Studies like these are building the case for a new theory of living systems. Although as yet there is no one coherent theory that ties it all together, as the body of evidence grows larger, science can no longer sweep the evidence under the rug.

The situation is similar to the early days of quantum theory when there was no single theory to explain what the scientists were uncovering. As discussed earlier, one physicist referred to the time between 1900 and 1925 as the Quantum Stone Age because scientists knew something was afoot but did not know how to explain it. Something similar is happening today. It is possible that this is another Stone Age, in that something much different than the worldview to which scientism adheres is becoming understood as the more appropriate explanation of the nature of living things, even if it cannot yet be fully explained or articulated in a coherent theory.

Regardless of whether or not a new theory emerges in the near future, the evidence continues to mount that life has a fundamental nonlocality in both the quantum domain and everyday world.

Chapter Notes

1. Jeans, quoted in Jahn, Robert and Brenda Dunne. "The Spiritual Substance of Science." In Jane Clark and Willis Harman (eds.). *New Metaphysical Foundations of Modern Science.* Sausalito, CA: Institute of Noetic Sciences, 1994: 164.

2. Bohr, quoted in Jahn and Dunne, "The Spiritual Substance of Science," p. 166.

3. Eddington, quoted in Wald, George. "The Cosmology of Life and Mind." In Jane Clark and Willis Harman (eds.). *New Metaphysical Foundations of Modern Science.* Sausalito, CA: Institute of Noetic Sciences, 1994: 130.

4. Folger, Tim. "Does the universe exist if we're not looking?" *Discover.* 23, no. 6 (June 2002): 44.

5. Ibid, pp. 44-47.

6. Ibid, p. 47.

7. Lind, quoted in Folger, "Does the universe exist if we're not looking?" p. 48.

8. Sirag, Saul-Paul. *Consciousness and Hyperspace.* Interview by Jeffrey Mishlove. Thinking Allowed Productions, 1998: 2. www.intuition.org/txt/sirag.htm.

9. Ibid, p. 5.

10. Ibid.

11. Herbert, Nick. *Quantum Reality.* New York: Anchor Books, 1985: 257.

12. Herbert, Nick. *Consciousness and Quantum Reality.* Interview by Jeffrey Mishlove. Thinking Allowed Productions, 1998: 5. www.intuition.org/txt/herbert.htm.

13. Targ, Russell and Jane Katra. *Miracles of Mind.* Novato, CA: New World Library, 1998: 54.

14. Dossey, Larry. *Reinventing Medicine.* New York: HarperCollins Publishers, 1999: 19.

15. O'Regan, Brendan and Caryle Hirshberg. *Spontaneous Remission: An Annotated Bibliography.* Sausalito, CA: Institute of Noetic Sciences, 1993.

16. Sicher, Fred, Elisabeth Targ, Dan Moore and Helene S.Smith. "A randomized double-blind study of the effect of distant healing in a population with advanced AIDS." *Western Journal of Medicine.* 169, no. 6 (Dec. 1998): 356-63.

17. Byrd, Randolph C. "Positive therapeutic effects of intercessory prayer in a coronary care unit population." *Alternative Therapies in Health and Medicine.* 3, no. 6 (Nov. 1997): pp. 87-90.

18. Dossey, Larry. *Healing Words: The Power of Prayer and The Practice of Medicine.* San Francisco: Harper San Francisco, 1993: 211.

19. Talbot, Margaret. "The placebo prescription." *The New York Times Sunday Magazine Online.* www.nytimes.com/library/magazine/home/20000109mag-talbot7.html. (9 Jan. 2000).

20. Brown, Walter. "The placebo effect." *Scientific American*. 278, no. 1 (Jan. 1998): 90-95.

21. Horrigan, Bonnie. "Papa Henry Auwae Po'okela la'au lapa'au: Master of Hawaiian medicine." *Alternative Therapies in Health and Medicine*. 6, no. 1 (Jan. 2000): 83.

22. Barasch, Marc. "A psychology of the miraculous." *Psychology Today*. 27, no. 2 (March/April 1994): 56.

23. *National Center for Complementary and Alternative Medicine*. www.nccam.com.

24. Ibid.

25. Dossey, *Reinventing Medicine*.

26. Rubik, Beverly. "Exploring the Frontiers of Science." Interview by Russell DiCarlo. *HealthWorld Online*, 1996: 3. www.healthy.net/asp/templates/interview.asp?PageType=Interview&ID=297. (1996).

27. Rubik, Beverly. *Frontier Science*. Interview by Daniel Redwood, 1999:2. www.drredwood.com/interviews/rubik.html.

28. Ibid, p. 3.

29. Rubik, "Exploring the Frontiers of Science," p. 8.

30. Ibid, pp. 7-8.

Seven

Creativity and Quantum Thinking

The television show of a few years back, "Quantum Leap," was a science fiction series about a man who continually jumped through time, overcoming barriers to the space-time continuum. Each week the series would show him in a different era facing various dilemmas.

The term quantum leap stems from Heisenberg's Uncertainty Principle. Heisenberg showed that for an electron, or any quantum object, there is only a probability of determining its position or speed, and that if the position is known, the speed can't be known, and vice-versa. This is due to the wave-particle nature of electrons and quantum objects, which are both in one place at one time and spread out everywhere. The quantum leap comes from the capability of the wave-particle to spread out everywhere, which leads to movement that can never be determined. It can jump from one area to another discontinuously in "lumps and jumps" without traveling through the intervening space. Thus, a particle in its quantum state can be anywhere and everywhere.

Of course, in the everyday world a particle can only be in one place at one time—obviously matter is not spread out everywhere. You will not find the chair you sit on, the table you eat at, or the bed you sleep on, anywhere but where you are accustomed to finding them. According to quantum physics, it is the act of measurement or observation that causes matter to occupy only one place. As Heisenberg said, "The path of the electron comes into existence only when we observe it."[1] Once measured, the particle is localized.

SCHROEDINGER'S CAT

The story of Schroedinger's cat is one of the best known examples of this quantum reality. Conceived as a thought experiment by Erwin Schroedinger, the story has been told in many variations, but always with the same twist ending. The cat is put inside an opaque box with a decaying radioactive particle. If the particle randomly decays one way, the cat gets food. If the particle decays another way, poison is released. Since there is a 50-50 chance that one or the other scenario will occur, the cat should be either dead or alive. Yet, in the quantum world, since all possibilities occur until a measurement is made, the cat will be both dead and alive until the box is opened and the cat is looked at.

Obviously, no one will see a cat that is both dead and alive. The cat will be either dead or alive. But in its quantum state the cat lives in all potential states. The change from many potential states to one actual state is known as the collapse of the wave function. What causes the collapse and whether it is a random physical event, or just a psychological event, is a great mystery.[2]

Nonetheless, just as quantum movement is discontinuous and occurs in an unpredictable and nonlinear fashion, so the collapse of the wave-function is also discontinuous because it occurs instantaneously (in a nonlocal universe, information can travel faster than the speed of light) and a continuous collapse would take time.[3]

If consciousness is also an aspect of the universe and contains a wave function, then consciousness can also transition discontinuously from all potential states into one specific location. This one location would be within the human mind. Anesthesiologist and professor of medicine Stuart Hameroff and mathematical physicist Roger Penrose, working collaboratively, have postulated the source of consciousness in the brain. They believe singular consciousness is created when the quantum state collapses, and the system must then choose a single universal state and decay and lock itself into that state. Their research has pinpointed this location to be in the microtubules of the brain.[4]

CONSCIOUSNESS AND CREATIVITY

Wherever and however the collapse of the wave function occurs, it is possible that its discontinuous and unpredictable movement can be seen as a creative one and as an aspect of the creative pulse of the universe. It could be that this creative pulse of the universe is an innate part of consciousness, both when it is spread throughout the universe in infinite positions, and in its singular position housed in the human mind. The physicist David Bohm once said, "Creativity is a fundamental principle of the Cosmos and what needed to be explained were the processes that were not creative."[5]

Aristotle and other Greek philosophers used the word *logos* as the root word for their system of logic. Logic has a connotation of reason, of rational intelligence. To the ancient Greeks the meaning of logos was a power that brings order to the world. To contemporary scientists-logicians the power that brings the world to order is reason, hence the relationship between logos, logic, and reason. However, the ancient Greeks saw logos as more than just reason. They saw it as the active creative principle, ever moving and changing. They also saw it as what they called *nous*, which they considered the world mind or universal intelligence.[6]

It could be, as Bohm said, that in a dynamic quantum universe, creative movement is the fundamental principle. If consciousness plays an important role in the universe, then consciousness is also part of this creative principle. This could explain the sometimes mysterious way that creativity works and how creative ideas often come when one is least expecting them, because creativity moves discontinuously.

Many have wondered about the source of creative ideas. Sometimes it seems as if creativity comes from a great unknown. The inventor Nicola Tesla said, "Creative ideas come to us like a bolt of lightning."[7] Albert Einstein once wondered, "Why is it I get my best ideas in the morning while I'm shaving?"[8] When physicist Steven Weinberg devised his electroweak theory, for which he won the Nobel Prize, he said it came to him in a flash one day, as he was driving his car to work.[9] In one of the most legendary stories, the Greek philosopher Archimedes was said to have made an important discovery about the displacement of water coinciding with the density of objects while he was taking a bath. It is said that Archimedes was so excited by his discovery that he jumped out of his tub and ran down the streets of his town, yelling "Eureka!" ("I found it!")[10]

History is filled with many stories of creative insights that arrived like flashes of light, whether in daydreams, creative reveries, or dreams. Most of the time the source of the creative idea falls outside the realm of logic and reason and instead emanates from a less definitive place. Often the springing forth of a creative idea is a Godelian, or quantum leap, out of the system. It is a discontinuous movement beyond formal logical thinking.

EINSTEIN'S BRAIN

When Albert Einstein died, scientists were curious about what made Einstein the genius he was. After his death in 1955, the pathologist at Princeton Hospital who was slated to perform the autopsy without the family's permission took it upon himself to remove and keep Einstein's brain. For the next forty years the pathologist stored the brain in jars of formaldehyde, studying it slice by slice under the microscope, and dispensing small chunks to other researchers who requested them. The goal was to discover the secrets of Einstein's genius.[11]

The pathologist never found any concrete proof, but one of his colleagues did. In the early 1980s, Marian Diamond, a neuroanatomist at the University of California at Berkeley announced what she believed to be the secret to Einstein's success. She found an increased number of glial cells in Einstein's left parietal lobe, a kind of neurological switching station that she described as an "association area for other association areas in the brain."[12] Glial cells act as a glue holding the other nerve cells together and also help transfer electrochemical signals between neurons. The neuroanatomist had expected to find these because research she had done with rats had found high glial cell concentrations in rats who had been given super-stimulating environments.[13]

This research may partly explain Einstein's brilliance, at least from a neuroanatomical perspective. However, more insight about it may come from Einstein himself. When asked how his thought processes worked, Einstein replied, "Words and language, whether written or spoken, do not seem to play any part in my thought processes. The psychological entities that serve as building blocks for my thought are certain signs or images, more or less clear, that I can reproduce and recombine at will."[14]

Einstein was saying that his thought processes were not purely linear and that a certain amount of imagery helped him work out his concepts. Perhaps this explains why Einstein, as a young man, had such a shoddy track record in school. He did not think in a purely linear way, which is the way the education system generally teaches. One teacher told the young Einstein, "You will never amount to anything."[15] Einstein was later expelled from high school and flunked his college entrance exam. By the time he was in his mid-twenties, no one could have predicted that Einstein, working as a civil servant in the Swiss patent office, would shortly shake the world with his revelations.[16]

QUANTUM THINKING

According to Danah Zohar in her book, *Rewiring the Corporate Brain*, there are three distinct ways of thinking. The first is the way of rational, logical, rule-bound thinking, what is called serial thinking. The second is associative, habit-bound thinking that allows for pattern-recognizing abilities, in which things are seen as interlinked. This is called parallel thinking. The third way is creative, rule-breaking, and rule-making thinking, a type of thinking that challenges assumptions, breaks habits, and changes mental models. This is quantum thinking.[17]

Quantum thinking is holistic, unifying, and integrating; it is capable of seeing the whole picture. As Zohar writes, "It unifies all the millions of data impinging on the brain at every moment into a field of experience with which we can deal. Quantum thinking itself seems to arise from a field across the brain built up by the synchronized oscillations of neurons from many different parts of the brain."[18]

Zohar also discusses how quantum and serial thinking impact on cognitive faculties. Serial thinking, she states, is the same thing as linear thinking, in that it follows the methodology of either-or, in which a statement is either true or false and there is just one right way to do things. This reflects the paradigm of Newtonian physics, where something is either a wave or a particle, either here or there, now or then.[19]

Quantum thinking follows the both-and approach of quantum theory, in which an entity is both particle-like and wave-like at the same time. This entity is present both here and now and simultaneously spreads out as possibilities everywhere in space and time. As it spreads out, it interconnects with members of other systems.[20]

Quantum thinking and creativity are closely interrelated, in that both are predicated on the discontinuous, nonlinear way in which quantum leaps in thinking are made, leading to insights that are considered beyond the conventional ways of thinking. This is akin to the way particle-waves move through the universe, jumping around discontinuously and unpredictably. The process of creativity seems mysterious, as if a switch were flipped in the mind that opened it to a greater way of thinking, one that connects it to the infinite quantum positions of which consciousness is part. If there is a literal or figurative switch that is flipped and it can be accessed, then it might hold the key to people being able to use more of their innate healing capabilities and more of their human potential. For a person to use more of his or her human potential, it entails using more of the mind's capacities and being able to quantum think and see the world from a broader perspective.

THE EDUCATIONAL SYSTEM

As I mentioned earlier, one major factor that keeps people from using his or her greater human potential is the education system. People are led to believe that the only place to practice creative thinking is while studying the arts, while other disciplines require a different mental framework and that if one does not become an artist, one will have no use for their creative thinking abilities. This cannot be true since art and science are one and the same, both springing forth from minds willing to make quantum leaps in thinking. Unfortunately, the way compartmentalized thinking patterns are formed is based on an educational system that is quite disconnected.[21] Disciplines are taught separately, leading to an inability to comprehend how things are interlinked and how each part is related to the whole.

In addition, during the educational process there is a lack of emphasis on creative thinking, except during the studying of the arts. Instead, the emphasis is on linear thinking and on disciplining the mind to find the one right answer, as Francis Bacon advocated. The inherent weakness of this system is that it creates a dichotomy in which perceptions are divided between right or wrong and boils choices down to absolutes of either/or, without making any allowance for gray areas in between. The linear thinking encouraged by the education system makes it virtually impossible to create new perceptions that cut across the chasm of absolute thinking.[22]

Although it is important for students to strengthen their logical thinking abilities and be able to discern between right and wrong, the problem with this approach is that it puts too much emphasis on critical thinking and not enough on constructive and creative thinking. With critical thinking, the student learns to analyze and find what is wrong with something. Every attempt is made to unpeel the model until all errors are removed. Edward de Bono has been a longtime advocate of a creative approach to education, and he writes:

> Is thinking that is free from error good thinking?...
> Critical thinking lacks the productive, generative, creative
> and design elements that are so needed to tackle prob-
> lems and find our way forward...Our traditional thinking
> system is based on "truth," which is to be uncovered and
> checked by logic and argument. The result is a strong
> tendency towards negativity and attack. Negativity is seen
> to be a powerful way of uncovering the truth.[23]

CRITICAL THINKING AND NEW IDEAS

Because this approach to critical thinking is one that attacks ideas to discern what is wrong with them, it causes the person doing the critical thinking to be quick to find fault with an idea and unlikely to embrace a new one. This is what happens to most new ideas, as the following example shows.

In 1959 a man living in Marin County, California, and working in San Francisco, devised a method to reduce his commuting time. He was tired of being stuck every day in his car because of the tollbooths on either side of the Golden Gate Bridge. There must be a way to save time, fuel consumption, and wear and tear on the vehicles, he thought. He came up with a revolutionary idea: why not have toll collectors on one side of the bridge and let the toll be double the one-way fare?

In this day and age that would hardly be considered a radical concept. However, in 1959 it had never been done before, and no one was sure if it was such a good idea. It flew in the face of common practice. The critical thinkers were able to tear apart the idea and find the errors inherent in it.

It wasn't until 1967, eight years later, that the idea was given a trial run. A new regional commissioner of transportation had been appointed, and since he was somewhat of a neophyte, he was not totally aware of all the "accepted" practices. He was willing to give it a shot and did. It was such a phenomenal success that within one year, bridge toll collecting across the country adopted the practice.[24]

There are countless examples of this sort. Here are a few more to further illustrate the point. In the mid-1800s in Vienna, Dr. Ignaz Semmelweis, an obstetrician, proposed that obstetricians wash their hands before delivering babies to lessen the possibility of spreading disease. He even proved his point by doing a study that showed how washing hands would lessen disease in newborns. The physicians involved refused to believe his idea could make a difference and ran him out of Vienna. He ended up committing suicide as a result of the emotional stress he suffered.[25]

In 1861, in Germany, Phillip Reiss invented a machine that could transmit music and was on the verge of inventing the telephone, but was persuaded there was no market for a telephone, because the telegraph was an adequate way to send messages. Fifteen years later Alexander Graham Bell invented the telephone.[26]

In 1938 Chester Carlson invented xerography. Virtually every major corporation, including IBM and Xerox, didn't think much of his idea and rejected it. They felt that since carbon paper was cheap and readily available, no one would buy an expensive copying machine.[27]

While a student at Yale, Fred Smith came up with the idea of Federal Express. Every delivery expert in the country, including the U.S. Postal Service and UPS, predicted such an idea would fail. Even his business professor at Yale said so. They all believed that no one would pay a higher price for overnight delivery.[28]

As these examples show, it is easy to think critically and tear an idea apart. It is much harder to think in a quantum way and be willing to create something new. Coming up with a new idea is the first part of the process, but the second and perhaps more difficult part is weathering the storm of criticism that is usually received for having broken from the pack. It is easier for most people to "group think" than to "quantum think" and to adhere to the belief that only artistically oriented people have creative thinking abilities and the right to use them. Unfortunately, because these limiting beliefs have become our society's mental models, many people are incapable of making quantum leaps in thinking, thereby contributing to their inability to tap into the greater human potential.

CREATIVE THINKING

Everyone has the ability to think creatively. It just needs to be cultivated and encouraged to allow for the expansion of worldviews and a better understanding of the limitations of rational thought. In other words, mental models based on a linear, deterministic viewpoint need to be expanded to include models that embrace nonlinear and quantum thinking.

There are many ways to accomplish this. Some say that in order to keep fresh and not become a victim of rigid thinking, one should make a major career change every ten years or so.[29] Business consultant Marsha Madigan believes it is the responsibility of leadership to help others actualize their creative potential.

> When leaders see the value of allowing space in between their thoughts, perspective in their thinking, they can see beyond the circumstances and content of problems and situations, to graceful responses and effortless solutions…If we want to change our experience, we need to let go of our current thinking in order to see something new. We need a stance of curiosity, of willingness to give up being "right," in order to see what we don't yet know, in order for a new reality to manifest through us.[30]

Others in the business world also recognize this need. One company executive says that when his design team gets bogged down, he will do something different, like take the entire group to the movies. "The tension began to dissipate," he says. "Within days ideas started flowing, knotty problem areas unraveled, and the design began to lead the designers, a sure sign that a strong concept was emerging."[31]

The comic actor John Cleese, who achieved fame as a member of the Monty Python comedy group, has also produced business training films. In them he parodies the mindset of logical thinking that he feels inhibits many companies from growing and prospering. Here are some of his suggestions about how best to stamp out creativity in an organization:

> One, always behave as though there's a war on. Two, strangle curiosity at birth—it may spread. Three, open all meetings by reciting the magic mantra, "The problem has not yet been born that cannot be cracked with more data and newer technology." Four, defend your preconceptions with your life! Five, if you spot a colleague engaging in unfamiliar activity such as wondering

out loud or gazing thoughtfully into space, poke them
with a sharp stick and accuse them of wasting time.
Finally, six, make the questioning of deadlines a capital
offense. If you're in a state which does not allow capital
punishment, relocate to Texas.[32]

Creative and quantum thinking can and should permeate all fields
and disciplines, including medicine, government, sports, and education.
It is a process that works in fits and starts; yet it is something we all are
capable of doing. In fact, some of the most creative people say the reason
they are so creative is that they strive for a quantity of ideas, knowing
they will have more bad than good ones. They are not afraid to have
bad ideas and are more than willing to throw the bad ones away.[33]

Ultimately, tapping into one's creative potential is a way to tap into
the creative potential of the universe. There are many ways to do so.
Some advocate inner disciplines such as meditation;[34] others advocate
creative thinking techniques.[35] These two approaches are not mutually
exclusive. Physicist and creativity researcher Amit Goswami says, "Using
outer creativity [creative techniques] to investigate inner creativity
[inner disciplines] is an age-old practice."[36] Zen does this by its use of
koans. The koans engage the mind and force students to use their outer
creativity to think outside the box. If the student does so and realizes
the essence of the koan, the student will have accessed his or her inner
creativity. In doing so, the student will have tapped into the creative
potential of the universe.

The ability to quantum think is to be able to think in the broadest
way possible. When people do such a thing, they are going beyond the
logical, linear way that most people are taught during their education.
By quantum thinking it may be possible to flip a switch in the mind and
body and open up new possibilities, possibilities that can trigger the
innate healing capabilities of the human body and release what humans
are potentially capable of doing. This will be discussed at length later
in the book.

Chapter Notes

1. Heisenberg, quoted in Goswami, Amit. *The Self-Aware Universe: How Consciousness Creates the Material World.* New York: Jeremy P. Tarcher/ Putnam, 1993: 39.

2. Lindley, David. *Where Does the Weirdness Go?* New York: BasicBooks, 1996: 61.

3. Goswami, *The Self-Aware Universe: How Consciousness Creates the Material World*, p. 40.

4. Hameroff, Stuart and Roger Penrose. "Orchestrated objective reduction of quantum coherence in brain microtubules: The orch OR model for consciousness." In Stuart Hameroff, W. Kaszniak and A.C. Scott (eds.). *Toward a Science of Consciousness: The First Tucson Conference Discussion and Debates.* Cambridge, MA: MIT Press, 1996.

5. Bohm, quoted in Falconar, Ted. *Creative Intelligence and Self-Liberation.* Bancyfelin, Carmarthen, Wales: Crown House Publishing, 2000: 55.

6. Rohmann, Chris. *A World of Ideas.* New York: Ballantine Books, 1999: 237.

7. Tesla, quoted in Goswami, Amit. *Quantum Creativity: Waking Up to Our Creative Potential.* Cresskill, NJ: Hampton Press, 1999: 67.

8. Einstein, quoted in Goswami, *Quantum Creativity: Waking Up to Our Creative Potential*, p. 164.

9. Glanz, James. "Physicist ponders God, truth, and a 'final theory.'" *The New York Times Online.* www.nytimes.com/library/national/science/012500sci-scientist-weinberg.html.(25 Jan. 2000).

10. Root-Bernstein, Robert and Michele Root-Bernstein. *Sparks of Genius.* New York:Houghton Mifflin, 1999: 40.

11. Wenger, Win and Richard Poe. *The Einstein Factor.* Rocklin, CA: Prima Publishing, 1996: 7-9.

12. Bower, Bruce. "Getting into Einstein's brain." *Science News.* 127 (May 25, 1985): 330.

13. Wenger and Poe, *The Einstein Factor*, pp. 7-9.

14. Einstein, quoted in Hadamard, Jacques. *An Essay on the Psychology of Invention in the Mathematical Field.* Princeton: Princeton University Press, 1945: 12.

15. West, Thomas, G. *In the Mind's Eye: Visual Thinkers, Gifted People with Learning Difficulties, Computer Images, and the Ironies of Creativity.* Buffalo, NY: Prometheus Books, 1991: 118.

16. Wenger and Poe, *The Einstein Factor*, p. 7.

17. Zohar, Danah. *Rewiring the Corporate Brain.* San Francisco: Berrett-Koehler, 1997: 26-37.

18. Ibid, p. 37.

19. Ibid, pp. 40, 55.

20. Ibid, pp. 54-55.

21. Root-Bernstein, *Sparks of Genius*, p. 22.

22. De Bono, Edward. *I Am Right, You Are Wrong.* New York: Penguin Putnam, 1990.

23. Ibid, pp. 6-7.

24. Firestien, Roger. *A Workshop on Consciousness and Creativity.* Held in Saratoga Springs, NY, March 30, 2001.

25. Dossey, Larry. "The forces of healing: Reflections on energy, consciousness, and the beef stroganoff principle." *Alternative Therapies in Health and Medicine.* 3, no. 5 (Sept. 1997): 9.

26. Michalko, Michael. *Cracking Creativity.* Berkeley: Ten Speed Press, 2001: 5

27. Ibid.

28. Ibid.

29. Csikszentamihalyi, Mihalyi. *Creativity: Flow and the Psychology of Discovery.* New York: HarperCollins, 1996: 145.

30. Madigan, Marsha. "Consciousness: A principle-based paradigm for leadership." *Business Spirit Journal Online*, Dec. 1999: 2-3. www.bizspirit.com/bsj/current/fea1.html.

31. Fisher, Anne. "Afternoon movies and other keys to creativity." *Fortune.* 140, no. 6 (Sept. 27, 1999): 242.

32. Cleese, John. "Basil Fawlty, manager." *Newsweek.* 133, no. 7 (Feb. 15, 1999): 47.

33. Csikszentmihalyi, Mihaly, and Robert Epstein. "A creative dialogue." *Psychology Today.* 32, no. 4 (July/August 1999): 60.

34. Goswami, *Quantum Creativity: Waking Up to Our Creative Potential,* p. 267.

35. Michalko, Michael. *Thinkertoys.* Berkeley: Ten Speed Press, 1991.

36. Goswami, *Quantum Creativity: Waking Up to Our Creative Potential,* p. 265.

Eight

Complexity, Self-Organization, and Medicine

As profound and provocative as quantum theory's implications are for understanding the true nature of the universe and for its relationship to health, human potential, and creative thinking, the quantum perspective still has its limitations. It is only one aspect of science, one whose viewpoint is from the standpoint of physics. And as fascinating and mind boggling a field as quantum theory is, it is only one part of the physics picture. Physics is not a homogenous field, but rather it is made up of two general areas—classical physics and modern physics, whose two main divisions are quantum mechanics and relativity theory. Other brilliant theories within modern physics have emerged in recent times, such as string theory and M theory. Those have added more substance to our understanding of the universe.

Not just physics, but moreover, the entire realm of science, is not a homogenous field. The historian of science, Thomas Kuhn, remarked in his book, *The Structure of Scientific Revolutions*, that the whole of science was once assumed to be a "single monolithic and unified enterprise that must stand or fall with any one of its paradigms as well as with all of them together."[1] Instead, said Kuhn, "Science is seldom or never like that…Viewing all fields together, it seems a rather ramshackle structure with little coherence among its various parts."[2] Kuhn also stated that what might be a revolutionary new approach for one scientific specialty may have no bearing on another specialty: "Though quantum mechanics is a paradigm for many scientific groups, it is not the same paradigm for them all."[3]

Some people have appropriated quantum theory in a partial way as a tool to explain many of the vast mysteries of life and in the process have given quantum theory an almost mystical aura. The truth is that quantum theory—and the whole of physics—is only dealing with mathematical abstractions and not with reality itself.

Although many of the early quantum physicists said and wrote things that had a philosophical and mystical tone, it was not because physics was explaining things in a mystical light. Instead, their scientific explorations were opening up new perspectives that went beyond physics. Physics of and by itself did not offer any answers about the spiritual nature of the universe, nor did it offer any support for a transcendental viewpoint. The early quantum physicists borrowed from eastern thought to help answer some of their questions about the true nature of the universe because they needed to find a language that spoke about what they were seeing, and the language of physics was not capable of doing that.

In their writings these early quantum physicists made clear that physics did not explain a spiritual universe. Einstein said, "The present fashion of applying the axioms of physical science to human life is not only entirely a mistake but has also something reprehensible in it."[4] Arthur Eddington wrote, "I do not suggest that the new physics 'proves religion' or indeed gives any positive grounds for religious faith...For my own part I am wholly opposed to any such attempt."[5] Even Erwin Schroedinger, who was a strong adherent of a mystical viewpoint, made his opinion clear: "It has nothing to do with it [mysticism]. Physics takes its start from everyday experience, which it continues by more subtle means. It remains akin to it, does not transcend it generically, it cannot enter into another realm. The attempt to do so is sinister."[6] James Jeans stated:

> What of the things which are not seen which religion assures us are eternal? There has been much discussion of late of the claims of scientific support for transcendental event. Speaking as a scientist, I find the alleged proofs totally unconvincing; speaking as a human being, I find most of them ridiculous as well.[7]

It was not that the physicists were negating a spiritual or mystical way of seeing the universe; on the contrary, most of them wholly embraced it. What they did not approve of was using physics as a way of rationalizing the spiritual aspects of life. To attempt to do so, they felt, was reductionism. These scientists were aware that physics and quantum theory are sciences of reductionism. As sciences that delve into the lowest levels of matter; they are about reducing matter to its smallest component. They understood that to extrapolate and say these lowest levels of matter represent the essence of reality is also reductionism.

Many contemporary physicists also have mystical perspectives. One scientist commented about them, "I have never met more metaphysical people than physicists."[8] Yet, they do not achieve their viewpoint purely through physics. Their view seems to emerge because they allow themselves to expand their outlook beyond one that only sees the world through the lens of scientism.

There are others, though, physicists and nonphysicists alike, who continue to maintain that quantum physics fully explains health and spirituality. One writer sums up this camp's attitude in a magazine article:

> Modern physics is replete with descriptions of the universe as a compilation of vibrations. Einstein's unified field theory states that all matter is organized energy. Energy is the electromagnetic expression of vibration. Quantum physics researchers have revealed that atoms, the building blocks of all form, consist of a vibrating neutron surrounded by particles that vibrate and spin wildly around it...When one of your body's systems, organs, or tissues functions improperly you become ill, or cellularly 'out-of-tune'...Disease, disorder and pain arise within portions of the vibratory continuum where information flows are restricted...Clearing such vibrational restrictions requires only the appropriate corrective vibration.[9]

Although positive health gains can be attained through clearing the body's vibrational restrictions, it is still a reductionist approach to state that all that is needed to achieve health is to have atoms vibrate properly. I have my doubts about a view that sees the atom the representative of perfect health. Humans are much more complex than that. Nobel laureate Charles Towne, the inventor of laser and maser, had this to say on the subject: "There seems to be no justification for the dogmatic position taken by some that the remarkable phenomenon of individual personality can be expressed completely in terms of the known laws governing the behavior of atoms and molecules."[10].

There is also the school of thought that believes all reality is created by the mind and that in essence everyone creates his or her own reality. This is predicated on the observer effect found in quantum physics, in which particles have a netherworld quality until a measurement is made, as was the case with Schroedinger's cat, who lived in a state of being both alive and not alive until the box was opened.

By subscribing to an "I create my own reality" school of thought, proponents of this are blurring the distinction between subjective and objective. While it is true that there is a relationship between the observer and the observed, there also is a distinct objective reality upon which the mind has no bearing. Again, the early quantum physicists were clear about this. Bohr stated, "In our future encounters with reality we shall have to distinguish between the objective and the subjective side, to make a division between the two."[11] Schroedinger said, "The pulling down of the frontier between observer and observed which many consider a momentous revolution of thought, to my mind seems a much overrated provisional aspect without profound significance."[12] And Louis de Broglie weighed in with the following:

> It has been said that quantum physics reduces or blurs the dividing region between the subjective and the objective, but there is…some misuse of language here. For in reality the means of observation clearly belong to the objective side; and the fact that their reactions on the parts of the external world which we desire to study cannot be disregarded in microphysics neither abolishes, nor even diminishes, the traditional distinction between subject and object.[13]

In the field of health, proponents of a world in which you create your own reality believe that health is achievable solely through the mind. However, there are many factors outside a person's control that impact on health, as the biopsychosocial model has shown. These factors include educational status, literacy, job satisfaction, religious practices, nutritional preferences, economic and social status, the effects of racial and gender bias, etc. Larry Dossey has pointed out that in a nonlocal universe, it is impossible to create your own reality. "There is considerable evidence (conclusive, in my mind) that I can create part of your reality and that you can create part of mine," he writes. "This is the conclusion from scores of studies in transpersonal imagery; distant EEG correlation studies; so-called 'bio-PK' experiments; and studies in the effects of distant, intercessory prayer. If we can affect the reality of each other, there is no basis for claiming that I am the sole architect of my reality."[14]

Because one school of Buddhism believes that people create their own reality, this belief has been promoted by some as a spiritual truth. If quantum physics gives a scientific explanation for spiritual concepts, the thinking goes, then quantum physics' observer effect proves what this school of Buddhism believes. But even that Buddhist belief is a misconception, as the Dalai Lama has stated:

> One such school (Vijnanvada, or Cittamatra, the Idealistic school of Mahayana Buddhist philosophy) asserts that there is no external reality, not even external objects, and that the material world we perceive is in essence merely a projection of our minds. From many points of view, this conclusion is extreme. Philosophically, and for that matter conceptually, it seems more coherent to maintain a position that accepts the reality not only of the subjective world of the mind but also of the external objects of the physical world.[15]

This does not negate what quantum theory says and its implications for health, creativity, and human potential. Instead, it is demonstrating that the picture has to be widened to encompass more accurately a broader landscape because quantum theory is not comprehensive enough to explain fully all phenomena. In other words, it is not extensive enough to be a true theory of everything by itself.

THE LIFE SCIENCES

To truly understand living systems in general and human beings in particular, physics is not the final arbiter. Instead, what needs to also

be taken into account and added to the equation are the sciences that
study living systems—the life sciences. As Fritjof Capra, the author of
The Tao of Physics, notes:

> Physics has now lost its role as the science providing the
> most fundamental description of reality…Scientists as
> well as nonscientists frequently retain the popular belief
> that "if you really want to know the ultimate explana-
> tion, you have to ask a physicist," which is clearly a
> Cartesian fallacy. Today the paradigm shift in science,
> at its deepest level, implies a shift from physics to the
> life sciences.[16]

The life sciences have gone through their own upheavals in recent times, having
been affected by chaos and complexity theory. It has been said that there have
been three great scientific revolutions in the physical sciences over the last 100
years: relativity, quantum mechanics, and now, chaos and complexity theory.
Chaos and complexity theory, unlike the other two, applies to the universe of
everyday experience. Because it applies to objects on a human scale, it has appli-
cability to the life sciences. Chaos and complexity theory also creates a bridge
between the world of quantum mechanics and the world of classical mechanics. They have attracted people from various fields, from physicists, biologists,
ecologists, mathematicians, computer scientists, biomedical and complementary
medicine practitioners to philosophers and artists. Like quantum theory, they
show that the world of linear determinism is not a true picture of the world. But
unlike quantum theory, they do so by looking at the nonlinear movements of
the everyday world.

Linear determinism assumes that if an action occurs, its effect can be
plotted. A small action is believed to cause a small effect. Double the size
of the action, it is presumed, and the effect is doubled. Linear systems are
predictable and controllable, and answers are given with confidence and an
aura of absolute authority. The answer might turn out to be totally wrong,
but because it is based on a logic that believes in the predictable nature of
life, it is felt that the outcome can be known with absolute certainty.

War and Linear Determinism

This illusion can sometimes have disastrous repercussions. For example,
in the Middle East in the fall of 1973, it appeared war was imminent

between Egypt, Syria, and Israel. The war that did break out came to be known as the Yom Kippur War. In the weeks leading up to the war, both Syria and Egypt started mobilizing forces at their respective borders with Israel. AMAN, the Israeli military intelligence agency, was aware of this. On October 6, 1973, one trusted intelligence source called and told Israel's director of military intelligence that Egypt and Syria would attack later that day. The Israeli cabinet called an emergency meeting to decide what to do, and whether to respond to the intelligence source that declared war imminent. The head of AMAN, Major General Eli Zeira, reviewed the evidence and proclaimed that war was not on the horizon and Israel was safe. He was wrong. Both Egypt and Syria attacked later that day, catching Israeli officials by surprise.[17]

After the Yom Kippur War was over, the Israeli government appointed an investigative panel to find out how Israel could have been caught by surprise. Major General Zeira, the head of AMAN, was called to testify and asked bluntly why he had insisted that war was not imminent. "The Chief of Staff has to make decisions, and his decisions must be clear," he replied. "The best support that the head of AMAN can give the Chief of Staff is to give a clear and unambiguous estimate, provided that it is done in an objective fashion. To be sure, the clearer and sharper the estimate, the clearer and sharper the mistake—but this is a professional hazard for the head of AMAN."[18]

Although Israel eventually won the Yom Kippur War, they had to scramble quickly to respond to the surprise attack. Zeira's desire to give a clear answer, whether right or wrong, led to the unwarranted deaths of many civilians who were unprepared for an attack. In the book *Military Misfortunes*, the historians Eliot A. Cohen and John Gooch lay the blame squarely on Zeira's doorstep and say it was his certainty that had proved fatal. "The culpable failure of AMAN's leaders in September and October 1973 lay not in their belief that Egypt would not attack but in their supreme confidence, which dazzled decision-makers," they wrote. "Rather than impress upon the prime minister, the chief of staff and the minister of defense the ambiguity of the situation, they insisted—until the last day—that there would be no war, period."[19]

The desire to speak with absolute authority, whether right or wrong, is the hallmark of deterministic thinking. In this case, there were profound and tragic consequences for doing so.

MEDICINE AND LINEAR DETERMINISM

This scenario happens all too often in life, and all too often in bio-medicine. A patient sees a physician and is given a medication or has a surgery that, they are told, will take care of their problem. Instead, the reverse occurs and they get worse. They may then be given another medication to take in addition to the first medication, or have additional surgery to "definitively" correct the problem. Because of biomedicine's adherence to a linear predictability, all things are believed to be capable of being fixed in a predictable manner, as if people were a set of pipes, and the physician, a plumber.

One person wrote of her own health tribulations in a magazine article entitled "An End to Painful Periods."[20] In the article, the author chronicles her story of dealing with endometriosis, with many failed surgeries and drug treatments. The final straw for her was when she decided to have a pre-sacral neurectomy. Her physician assured her she had a 90% chance of ending her years of torturous and cramping pain. Even though the surgery could result in a loss of sexual feeling, bladder problems, and constipation and even though she would have to go on the drug Synarel, which would induce a state of medical meno-pause (and she was only 20 years old at the time), she was willing to go through with it because of her physician's assurances.

Three days after surgery, she wrote, "My period started again with the same torturous cramps. I refused to talk with my doctor."[21] The Synarel did give her some pain relief, but after the maximum six-month period of taking it, the pain returned. Here she was, having had radical medical procedures based on empty assurances, no better than when she started. In fact, because of the radical procedures, she was worse. Ultimately, she found her way to acupuncture and Chinese medicine. She concluded her article by stating, "Today, as a 24-year-old, I've achieved almost total remission after two years of regular acupuncture treatment."[22]

CHINESE MEDICINE AND COMPLEXITY

Chinese medicine, which is based on Chinese philosophy, has always maintained a less deterministic way of looking at the body and at nature. It has come to the understanding that there are many complexities in life that cause many unpredictable things to occur. Life is seen as a great web, with action occurring in wavelike motions. It is believed that an action in one area of the web can cause an indeterminable effect in another area of the web. The late biochemist and Sinologist Joseph Needham explains:

> China and Europe differed most profoundly perhaps in the great debate between continuity and discontinuity; just as Chinese mathematics was always algebraic rather than geometrical, so Chinese physics was faithful to a prototypic wave theory and perennially averse to atoms. There is no doubt that the Buddhist philosophers were bringing in knowledge of the Vaiseshika theories about atoms, but nobody in China was willing to listen. The Chinese stuck to the ideas of universal motion in a continuous medium, action at a distance, and the wavelike motions of yin and yang.[23]

One contemporary book on acupuncture and Chinese medicine, by the late Japanese acupuncturist Yoshio Manaka, has even attempted to use chaos and complexity theory to explain how Chinese medicine works. What Dr. Manaka writes is that chaos and complexity theory have shown that living systems can spontaneously give rise to order, and in the body's energy system, this order can be seen as a flow and inter-relationship between the body's meridians and biorhythms. Manaka feels that order in the body refers to synchronous harmonic effects, or resonances, that occur in the meridians and biorhythms. According to Manaka's theory, the effectiveness of acupuncture is caused by its giving rise to order in the body by creating synchronization and resonance among the body's systems.[24]

TURBULENCE AND COMPLEXITY

What Chinese medicine and philosophy understood and what Western science and medicine are only realizing is that there are many factors that play a role in determining the end result of something and that many of these factors cannot be predicted. This is due to turbulence, instability that transforms order into disorder, predictability into seemingly random and chaotic motion, and breaks rules and refuses to conform to the norm. It is said that as Heisenberg lay on his deathbed, he claimed he would have two questions for God: why relativity and why turbulence? Heisenberg replied, "I really think He may have an answer to the first question."[25]

Turbulence leads to predictions that are virtually impossible because of its complex nature, and something that has a complex nature contains an incredible amount of diversity. In Chapter One we discussed the common cold and the difficulty biomedicine has with it. This difficulty can be traced to the complex and diverse nature of viruses and the fact they do not follow predictable patterns. By not following predictable patterns, it is very difficult for viruses to be controlled because they seem to have a mind of their own and replicate at will within the body.

All life operates in a complex and diverse pattern, and as researchers have shown, all systems—biological, cognitive, and social—also function in this way. The nature of life is complex and diverse. Yet it is not random and chaotic; there is an order to it. This order is created by the innate sense of organization, or self-organization, as it is more appropriately called, within living systems. Joseph Needham remarked about this phenomenon in 1935 when he wrote, "A logical analysis of the concept of organism leads us to look for organizing relations at all levels, higher and lower, coarse and fine, of the living structure."[26]

The science of complexity is an outgrowth of the study of chaotic systems. The science of chaos was the first to map out the nonlinear movement of systems. Its official beginning was in the mid-1960s when a research meteorologist named Edward Lorenz at the Massachusetts Institute of Technology was feeding numbers into a computer to predict weather patterns. He discovered that if he made a small change in the data, the end result in weather would be radically different than data without the small change. He found that for each small change he entered, very different weather patterns would result. He realized that systems are highly sensitive and dependent on initial conditions. He coined this the "Butterfly Effect" and put forth the concept that a butterfly that flaps its wings in China today could effect the weather in Florida tomorrow.[27]

Since that time chaos theory has more fully explored nonlinear dynamics and has led researchers to the discovery that there is an underlying order to what at first appears to be pure random chaos. The study of this underlying order has developed into the science of complexity. Complexity is considered to be the boundary between order and chaos. More precisely, complexity lies at the edge of chaos, which is the critical band where systems display the greatest complexity and where transformation and the emergence of new properties can potentially occur.[28]

Complexity theory is also related to what is known as the systems view of life. Systems theory seeks to find the underlying commonality of a living system, especially in terms of its organization. It does not reduce things to their smallest components. Instead, a systems view sees living systems as integrated wholes whose properties cannot be reduced to smaller parts. The properties of the system are realized from the synergy of all components working together; by themselves, the parts are not seen as having these properties. Instead, the properties of the system arise from the "organizing relations" (as Needham called them) of the parts.[29] The systems view subscribes to the adage that the whole is greater than the sum of its parts.

SELF-ORGANIZATION

Complexity theory is an outgrowth of systems theory and looks at the process of self-organization of living systems. What is becoming clear through the study of complexity is that the process of self-organization is intrinsic to the evolution and progression of a living system. In self-organization there is a harmony among the component parts, manifesting as a synchronization, or unity among the parts, and leading towards the creation of a greater whole and the emergence of new properties. Because complexity occurs at the edge of chaos, it may be that what at first appears as random and chaotic movements might instead be a movement towards self-organization and ultimately towards the evolution of a living system into something new.

The concept of synchronization is one that researchers have been looking into for quite some time, with the hope it may tell them more about the nature of self-organization. One of the most famous examples of this is the study that showed that women living together in close quarters end up with synchronous menstrual cycles.[30]

A synchronization factor has even been found with inanimate objects such as pendulum clocks. Christiaan Huygens, the seventeenth century contemporary of Newton, was an astronomer and inventor who designed and built the first pendulum clock. When he tested a pair of clocks at sea, he saw a phenomenon which baffled him and which scientists only now are beginning to understand. When he had the clocks side by side, he found that even when they began to get out of "sync," they soon got into a rhythm in which the pendulum of one moved as if it were a mirror image of the other. Through the contemporary tools of nonlinear dynamics and chaos theory, researchers have been able to comprehend more fully the conditions that allow for synchronizations such as this one to occur.[31]

In another line of research in the field, the late neurobiologist Francisco Varela studied synchronization in the brain. It showed that the brain recognizes perceptions through the process of synchronization of neuronal activity. When something that is viewed is recognized, millions of neurons throughout the brain erupt in a pattern of electrical firings. All of these firings then synchronize, allowing for the brain to recognize what has been perceived. Varela found that in essence the process of synchronization of the various sectors of the brain creates consciousness, or self-awareness.[32]

Varela began his scientific career by studying the complex information network that exists in living systems. Along with his colleague Humberto Maturana, he coined the term *autopoiesis*, or self-making, to explain the way he believed the information network operated. Autopoiesis is a network pattern in which the function of each component is to participate in the production or transformation of other components in the network. In this way the network continually makes and renews itself. It is produced by its components, and in turn it produces its components.[33]

What the two scientists believe they found is that the organization of a living system is the set of relations among its components that characterize the system as belonging to a particular class (such as a bacterium, a sunflower, a cat, or a human brain). The description of that organization is an abstract description of relationships and does not identify the components. Varela and Maturana assumed that autopoiesis is a general pattern of organization common to all living systems, whatever the nature of their components.[34]

They believe that autopoiesis is common to all living systems. It is a network of production processes, in which the entire network continually "makes itself." "In a living system," according to Varela and Maturana, "the product of its operation is its own organization."[35]

In the business world self-organization is starting to be seen as an innate quality of organizations. Jeffrey Goldstein, in *The Unshackled Organization*, offered this:

> Self-organization is not hierarchically driven. Instead, it is a process of system transformation that is self-generating. Self-organization happens when a work group or an organization is facing a challenge and is allowed to respond to that challenge in a spontaneous, unshackled manner...A work group or organization as a natural system will spontaneously know how to reorganize in the face of a challenge, if the obstacles hindering its capacity to self-organize are removed.[36]

Two researchers studying organizations and their capability to self-organize concluded that for self-organization to occur four elements must be present: 1) a sufficient degree of boundary openness; 2) an experimenting capacity; 3) an awareness of deep structure, in terms of shared values and vision; and 4) an ability to repair boundaries and move as a whole, shifting and adjusting to meet the non-equilibrium conditions present.[37]

If it is true that a sufficient degree of boundary openness is required for a system to self-organize, this would parallel the Godelian view of the universe as infinite and open-ended. This is in contrast to the deterministic view that all life follows set patterns, and is finite and decaying, as dictated by the laws of thermodynamics. The first law of thermodynamics deals with the conservation of energy, the second law with entropy. According to entropy, eventually everything runs down and decays.

Yet, the laws of thermodynamics apply only to closed or isolated systems, such as machines. Life, on the other hand, is an open system that engages with its environment and continues to grow and evolve.[38] Unfortunately, most people have it ingrained in their head that the laws of thermodynamics, and especially entropy, are inevitable and absolute facts of life. This leads people to the only logical conclusion that can be had from these laws: the universe is marching towards a certain death.

Biologist James Lovelock, author of *The Gaia Hypothesis* refutes that and says, "The laws of thermodynamics read like the notice at the gates of Dante's Hell."[39]

Studies and concepts such as the ones above that tell us we live in an open-ended and self-organizing universe led George Leonard to write: "At the heart of each of us, whatever our imperfections, there exists a silent pulse of perfect rhythm, a complex of waveforms and resonances, which is absolutely individual and unique, and yet which connects us to everything in the universe. The act of getting in touch with this pulse can transform our personal experience and in some way alter the world around us."[40]

Biomedicine and Complexity

Science has shown that life moves in these complex patterns, self-organizing into new patterns that are often unpredictable. These new patterns are considered emergent properties, which is the creation of new and higher levels of order. Yet, for all that science has shown as to the complexities of life, biomedicine still continues in its set way, stuck behind the wheel of linear determinism. One physician, concurring with the opinion that biomedicine no longer gives a full and valid description of life, wrote an article in the Journal of the American Medical Association in which he stated that "American medicine is one of the last bastions of the modernist belief that all things are potentially knowable." He went on to write that the ability to know all things, based on a deterministic logic, is a fallacy, and that chaos theory needs to be integrated into medicine.[41]

He must have hit a raw nerve, because he was met by a chorus of rebutting physicians who protested: "Medicine still maintains a degree of reliability and predictability"; "Chaos theory is still a theory"; and "Quackery is sure to flourish" if chaos theory gains a stronghold in medicine.[42]

Other researchers in the biomedical field are not as quick to denounce chaos and complexity theory because they have studied the complex network that comprises the human body. Physiologist Ary Goldberger and his associates have discovered that the heart and other physiological systems behave most erratically when they are young and healthy. Conversely, he has found that increasingly regular behavior sometimes accompanies aging and disease. What he has concluded is that irregularity and unpredictability are important features of health and that decreased variability and accentuated periodicities are associated with disease.[43]

Another team of researchers applying complexity theory to cancer has concluded: "Cancer is a process that outwardly appears to follow a linear path from normal tissue to host death. If one looks closer, however, carcinogenesis displays characteristics that are chaotic in nature and, upon even closer examination, cancer can be viewed as a complex adaptive system."[44]

A complex adaptive system, which is a type of self-organization, is one in which a living system acquires information about its environment and its own interaction within that environment, and then adjusts itself into a new model in accordance with the information it has received.[45] It could be that not only cancer, but all illness, has a complex adaptive mechanism that takes place within the body. It may be that the entire body is sharing information with itself and in the process creating a complex adaptive system.

Findings such as these have led two physicians to write in the *British Medical Journal*:

> Illness arises from dynamic interaction within and between systems [of the body], not from failure of a single component...Neither illness nor human behavior is predictable and neither can safely be "modeled" in a simple cause and effect system. The human body is not a machine and its malfunctioning cannot be adequately analyzed by breaking the system down into its component parts and considering each in isolation. Despite this fact, cause and effect modeling underpins much of the problem solving we attempt in clinical encounters; this perhaps explains why we so often fail.[46]

When applied to biomedicine, chaos and complexity theory do not invalidate or eliminate the need for a reductionist science. Rather, they help broaden the scope of understanding, allowing for a wider array of phenomena to be understood. Chaos and complexity theory goes beyond the metaphor of the body as a machine, and by doing so it challenges the practitioner to view the body as an interconnected web of information.

Chapter Notes

1. Kuhn, Thomas. *The Structure of Scientific Revolutions*. Chicago: University of Chicago Press, 1962: 49.

2. Ibid.

3. Ibid, p. 50.

4. Einstein, quoted in Planck, Max. *Where is Science Going?* New York: Norton, 1932: 209.

5. Eddington, Arthur Stanley. *New Pathways in Science*. New York: Macmillan, 1935: 307-08.

6. Schroedinger, Erwin. *Science, Theory, and Man*. New York: Dover, 1957: 204.

7. Jeans, James. *The Mysterious Universe*. Cambridge: Cambridge University Press, 1931: 117.

8. Glanz, James. "Reconciling nothingness in the universe and the soul." *The New York Times Online*. (Dec. 7, 1999): 3. www.nytimes.com/library/national/science/120799sci-essay-nothingness.html.

9. Trembath, Michael. "Vibrational healing and Samvahan massage." *WellBeing Magazine*. No. 64 (1999): 36.

10. Towne, Charles. "Gathering of the realms: the convergence of science and religion." *Science and Spirituality*. 10, no. 1 (1999): 18-19.

11. Bohr, Niels. *Atomic Physics and Human Knowledge*. New York: Wiley, 1958: 74.

12. Schroedinger, Erwin. *Nature and the Greeks*. Cambridge: Cambridge University Press, 1954: 15.

13. De Broglie, Louis. *Matter and Light*. New York: Dover, 1946: 252.

14. Dossey, Larry. "Antonovsky's perspective may not go far enough." *Advances: The Journal of Mind-Body Health*. 10, no. 3 (Summer 1994): 15.

15. Dalai Lama. *Mindscience*. Boston: Wisdom Publications, 1991: 15.

16. Capra, Fritjof. *The Web of Life*. New York: Anchor Books, 1996: 13.

17. Gladwell, Malcolm. "Connecting the dots." *The New Yorker*. (March 10, 2003): 83.

18. Ibid, p. 88.

19. Ibid.

20. Hochgesang, Jennifer. "An end to painful periods." *Natural Health*. (July-August, 1998): 76-80.

21. Ibid, p. 78.

22. Ibid, p. 80.

23. Needham, Joseph. *Science in Traditional China*. Cambridge, MA: Harvard University Press, 1981: 11.

24. Manaka, Yoshio. *Chasing the Dragon's Tail*. Brookline, MA: Paradigm Publications, 1995: 28.

25. Gleick, James. *Chaos: Making a New Science*. New York: Penguin Books, 1987: 121.

26. Needham, quoted in Haraway, Donna Jeanne. *Crystals, Fabrics, and Fields: Metaphors of Organicism in Twentieth-Century Developmental Biology*. New Haven: Yale University Press, 1976: 139.

27. Gleick, *Chaos: Making a New Science*.

28. Zohar, Danah. *Who's Afraid of Schroedinger's Cat?* New York: Quill/William Morrow, 1997: 134.

29. Capra, *The Web of Life*, p. 36.

30. Angier, Natalie. "How biology affects behavior and vice versa." *The New York Times*. (May 30, 1995): C7.

31. Noble, Ivan. "Centuries-old puzzle solved." *BBC News Online*. (Feb. 20, 2002): 2 http://news.bbc.co.uk/low/english/sci/tech/newsid_1820000/1820643.stm.

32. Stein, Ron. "Tracing the brain's obscure path to perception." *The Washington Post*. (Feb. 22, 1999): D7.

33. Capra, *The Web of Life*, p. 162.

34. Ibid, p. 98.

35. Maturana, Humberto, and Varela, Francisco. *Autopoiesis and Cognition*. London: Reidel, 1980: 82.

36. Goldstein, in Dove, Rick. "Enterprise Mandelbrots and self-organization." *Automotive Production*. 108, no. 10 (Oct. 1996): 17.

37. Ehin, Charles. "The ultimate advantage of self-organizing systems." *Journal for Quality and Participation*. 18, no. 5 (Sept. 1995): 33.

38. Wheatley, Margaret J. *Leadership and the New Science*. San Francisco: Berrett-Kohler, 1999: 77.

39. Lovelock, James. *Gaia*. New York: Oxford University Press, 1987: 123.

40. Leonard, George. *The Silent Pulse*. New York: E.P. Dutton, 1978: xii.

41. Goodwin, James S. "Chaos and the limits of modern medicine." *Journal of the American Medical Association*. (Nov. 5, 1997): 1399-1400.

42. Theodoropoulos, Demetrios S., Farrin A. Manian and James S. Goodwin. "Modern medicine and chaos theory (includes reply)" (Letter to the

editor). *Journal of the American Medical Association.* (March 18, 1998): 835-36.

43. Goldberger, Ary L., David R. Rigney and Bruce J.West. "Chaos and fractals in human physiology." *Scientific American.* (Feb. 1990): 44.

44. Schwab, E.D. and K.J. Pienta. "Cancer as a complex adaptive system." *Medical Hypotheses.* 47, 3 (Sept. 1996): 236.

45. Gell-Mann, Murray. *The Quark and the Jaguar.* New York: W.H. Freeman and Company, 1994: 17.

46. Wilson, Tim and Tim Holt. "Complexity and clinical care." *British Medical Journal.* 323 (Sept. 2001): 685.

Nine

Dawn of a New Consciousness

Although the addition of chaos and complexity to the scientific picture adds more depth to an understanding of life, nature, and the universe, when all is said and done, it is still a science that gives a physical and quantitative description of the universe. While quantum and complexity theories give a better framework for comprehending the nuances and gray areas of life, as opposed to a deterministic approach, which can only see things in terms of black and white, the new sciences are not fully capable of saying much about the qualitative aspects of life. Lewis Thomas was aware of this when he wrote, "The only solid piece of scientific truth about which I feel totally confident is that we are profoundly ignorant about nature...It is this sudden confrontation with the depth and scope of ignorance that represents the most significant contribution of twentieth-century science to the human intellect."[1]

In writing this, Thomas is expressing his awareness of the limitations of the scientific way. The scientific way searches for truth, yet truth cannot be fully uncovered by equations, experiments, and clinical trials. The scientific way can say profound things about its section of the universe; yet there are other sections of the universe that science cannot fully touch. Questions such as, "What is mind?" and "What is consciousness?" can not be easily answered within the domain of science. Richard Feynman put it well when he wrote: "The next great era of awakening of human intellect may well produce a method of understanding the qualitative content of equations...Today we cannot see whether Schroedinger's equation contains frogs, musical composers, or morality—or whether it does not. We cannot say whether something beyond it like God is needed or not."[2]

"I would add that not one of these fascinating questions [about the nature of life] is likely to depend on the latest wrinkles in particle physics or early-universe cosmology," writes the physicist Frank Wilczek. "When and if we have found the complete irreducible laws of physics, we certainly shall not thereby know the mind of God (Hawking to the contrary). We will not even get much help in understanding the minds of slugs, which is about the current frontier of neuroscience."[3]

Science cannot say much about the qualitative aspects of life, such as whether frogs are contained in Schroedinger's equations, or what is the mind of God, since that is not its job. However, that does not negate the role of science when it comes to pursuing these questions. Instead, it means the boundaries of thinking have to be pushed farther in order to incorporate a broader framework.

Although the new sciences have shown the interconnectedness of all of life, they are not capable of fully explaining this interconnectedness, since much of this explanation lies beyond the physical sciences. To explore interconnectivity more capably would entail integrating various concepts that have a seemingly antagonistic relationship, such as science and spirituality, rationality and intuition, art and science, biomedicine and alternative medicine, in order to cover every section of the universe. Bringing together different threads would amount to the forging of a true theory of everything, one that could bring together the hard realities of empirical science with the soft but irrefutable realities of the interior and conscious domain.

THE HARMONY OF OPPOSITES

Chinese philosophy has always understood this integration. In Chinese philosophy the ultimate goal is to achieve a union and harmony of opposites. It teaches that everything springs forth from one indivisible source, the Tao, and that all things (what are called the "10,000 things") are differentiated aspects of the Tao. In bringing opposites together, it is understood their union creates a synergy in which the Tao can more effectively be recognized and realized.[4]

Chinese philosophy is reminiscent of the Principle of Complementarity, an axiom of quantum mechanics postulated by Niels Bohr. Bohr came to the understanding that an electron can be both a wave and particle. He maintained that the particle and wave were complementary; that is, they were both necessary to give a complete picture of the electron, even though they were mutually exclusive. Bohr deeply believed that complementarity extended beyond physics to the level of everyday experience. India's eminent physicist D. S. Kothari expressed this view:

> The Principle of Complementarity...is perhaps the most significant and revolutionary concept of modern physics. The complementary approach can enable people to see that seemingly irreconcilable points of view need not be contradictory. These, on deeper understanding, may be found to be complementary and mutually illuminating—the two opposing contradictory aspects being parts of a "totality," seen from different perspectives. It allows the possibility of accommodating widely divergent human experiences into an underlying harmony, and bringing to light new social and ethical vistas for exploration and for alleviation of human suffering. Bohr fervently hoped that one day complementarity would be an integral part of everyone's education and provide guidance in the problems and challenges of everyday life.[5]

Bohr was well aware that the principle of complementarity was mirrored in the union of opposites in the philosophies of the East. When he was knighted by the Danish king and had to design a coat of arms, he chose for it the Taoist symbol of yin and yang, which in his view illustrated perfectly the principle he had articulated in physics.

THE INTEGRAL WAY

This approach of finding the harmony of opposites is known in modern times as the integral way. Integral means to integrate, to bring together, to join, to link, and to embrace.[6] The integral approach attempts to look at things from the largest and broadest perspective possible. It does so not in an eclectic manner, but by providing a consistent and systematic vision that combines truths from various fields, such as physics (including quantum physics) and biology; chaos and complexity theory; biomedicine and alternative medicine; chemistry and neuroscience; art, poetry and aesthetics in general; psychology and philosophy; and mysticism and spirituality. The common ground in an integral approach is to find the unifying thread amongst all the fields and amongst all truths.

For example, on an analysis of the field of consciousness, many definitions of consciousness are found, all based on the various schools of thought within the field. Many of the schools of thought stubbornly insist theirs is the true picture. However, what if each had a share of the truth? Ken Wilber has suggested, "Instead of asking which approach is right and which is wrong, we assume each approach is true but partial, and then try to figure out how to fit these partial truths together, how to integrate them—not how to pick one and get rid of the others."[7]

Using an integral approach, Wilber has outlined each of the competing theories of consciousness:

1.   Cognitive Science—views consciousness as anchored in functional schemas of the brain-mind.

2.   Introspectionism—maintains that consciousness is best understood in terms of intentionality, anchored in first person accounts.

3.   Neuropsychology—views consciousness as anchored in neural systems, neurotransmitters, and organic brain mechanisms.

4.   Individual Psychotherapy—views consciousness as primarily anchored in an individual organism's adaptive capacities.

5.   Social Psychology—views consciousness as embedded in networks of cultural meaning or as a byproduct of the social system itself.

6.   Clinical Psychiatry—views consciousness in strictly neurophysiological and biological terms.

7. Developmental Psychology—views consciousness not as a single entity but as a developmentally unfolding process.

8. Psychosomatic Medicine—views consciousness as strongly and intrinsically interactive with organic bodily processes.

9. Nonordinary States of Consciousness—views consciousness as a realm that encompasses states outside our everyday, waking realm.

10. Eastern and Contemplative Traditions—views consciousness as a spectrum in which ordinary consciousness is but a narrow and restricted version of deeper or higher modes of awareness.

11. Quantum Consciousness—views consciousness as capable of interacting and altering the physical world, through quantum interactions at the intracellular level and in the material world at large.

12. Subtle Energies Research—believes that there are subtler types of bioenergies beyond the four recognized forces of physics and that these play an intrinsic role in consciousness and its activity.[8]

In mapping out these various schools of thought, Wilber has attempted to find a common ground, a unifying theme for the inherent contradictions that some of these schools pose. In an effort to unite them in an integral manner, he proposes a higher ground where a theory of consciousness can find a new synthesis. If this type of integral thinking is followed to its conclusion, it may be possible to allow for consciousness to be seen as a natural phenomenon, falling under the sway of natural laws.

An integral approach has similarities to the teachings of the German philosopher Georg Hegel (1770-1831). In Hegel's view existence is a dialectical process of thesis, antithesis, and synthesis, through which two contradictory forces are resolved in a higher, more rational state.

He believed that the fullest expression of reason and rationality was its ability to unify opposites and see the identity that comes out of the differences.[9] Hegel saw history as the progressive development of human understanding toward perfect knowledge; he believed civilization advances in stages, or "historical moments," each of which is a necessary but incomplete step in the development of human consciousness, reason, and freedom. Since each stage is imperfect, he postulated, its flaws give rise to opposing ideas of forces, and out of the resulting conflict comes a new, higher, and temporarily more stable stage, what he considered the synthesis of ideas.[10]

The integral approach understands that all perspectives interrelate and interconnect: art, business, religion, medicine, science, sports, culture. The list of interrelationships is endless. Sri Aurobindo (1872-1950), the Indian sage who was one of the first to promote an integral philosophy, wrote, "The integral knowledge admits the valid truths of all views of existence, valid in their own field, but it seeks to get rid of their limitations and negations and to harmonize and reconcile these partial truths in a larger truth which fulfills all the many sides of our being in the one omnipresent Existence."[11]

Aurobindo defined the "one omnipresent Existence" as the Divine, or Spirit. Spirit's relationship with humanity, Aurobindo believed, was two fold: we were meant, through evolution, to ascend towards Spirit, and Spirit was meant, through involution, to descend into humanity. "If there is such a Divinity, Self or Reality, it must be everywhere, one and indivisible, nothing can possibly exist apart from its existence," he wrote in *The Life Divine*. "Our reason tells us, our intuitive consciousness feels, and their witness is confirmed by spiritual experience, that the one pure and absolute Existence exists in all things and beings even as all things and beings exist in It and by It, and nothing can be or happen without this indwelling and all supporting Presence."[12]

Aurobindo maintained that the Divine, since it is everywhere, is also in man as a partially concealed spirit. Through spiritual disciplines one is able to break through to a greater awareness of this more authentic Self, which is not independent of the superficial ego that is presented to the world.[13] He went on to state, "The obstacle to the achievement of the aims of this spiritual discipline is not the material limitations of the natural world. It is the failure to seek the inner self that is already a higher consciousness."[14]

In Aurobindo's integral view there is a place for both spirituality and materialism, for both the mystical and analytical. He knew it would be an important advance if he could discover the means to connect personal religious experience with the modern world's larger but inherently non-religious analytical rationality. He was able to do so by placing them within a continuum, arguing that within this continuum people progress from partial truth to a more complete truth. This process does not place differences in irreconcilable contradiction but rather in a larger conceptual context.[15]

An integral worldview says the universe is inclusive of a spiritual dimension, thus making a place for both science and spirituality. Because the integral worldview attempts to see things from the broadest possible perspective, it runs parallel to the concept of quantum thinking. From the quantum perspective, an idea, like an electron, spreads out across the universe in infinite patterns and positions and then interconnects with all other ideas, creating, as the early quantum physicists understood, a universe that is pure mind.

APERSPECTIVAL

The Swiss philosopher Jean Gebser (1905-1973) called the integral worldview an aperspectival one, as opposed to what he called a perspectival and unperspectival one.[16] He saw perspectival and unperspectival as opposites, while aperspectival was considered a new way of thought, one of liberation from exclusive and limiting perspectives. Gebser believed that around the thirteenth century the unperspectival age began to change and evolve into the perspectival age, and by the fourteen and fifteenth centuries, during the time of the Renaissance, the evolution from unperspectival to perspectival was completed. Now, in very recent times, the perspectival age is giving way to an aperspectival, or integral, age.

Gebser explains the difference between the unperspectival and perspectival epochs as follows:

> In very general terms we might say that the unperspectival world preceded the world of mind- and ego-bound perspective discovered and anticipated in late antiquity and first apparent in Leonardo's application

> of it. Viewed in this manner the unperspectival world
> is related to the anonymous "one" or tribal "we," the
> perspectival to the "I" or Ego; the one world is grounded
> in Being, the other, beginning with the Renaissance,
> in Having; the former is predominantly irrational, the
> later rational.[17]

According to Gebser, it was during the Renaissance that the perspectival era came to fruition. The key was the "discovery of perspective which opened up the three-dimensionality of space."[18] This was an important intellectual milestone which flowered during the Renaissance and found its great achievements in the work of scientists such as Newton, Bacon, and Descartes and in artists such as Da Vinci (though Da Vinci was both scientist and artist) and Michaelangelo. Gebser also believed that with the onset of the twentieth century another new era, the aperspectival age, sprouted up, and with it the heralding of the dawn of a new consciousness. The belief in this aperspectival age has been supported not only by findings in modern physics, but also by developments in the arts and humanities, in which "the incorporation of time as a fourth dimension into previously spatial conceptions has formed the initial basis for manifesting this new consciousness."[19]

Aperspectivalism is a pluralistic, multiple-perspectives view, in contrast to formal rationality, or perspectival reason, which tends to take a single, set perspective and view all reality through that narrow lens.[20]

The truth is, however, that the flowering of an integral-aperspectival age has been envisioned for a long time. Mystics, artists, and philosophers have long railed against what they felt were the limitations of the perspectival way. In 1802, the poet William Blake wrote his famous poem "Newton's Sleep": "May God us keep/From single vision and Newton's sleep."[21]

Even before the twentieth century's dramatic findings helped usher in an aperspectival age, some scientists were realizing that a perspectival approach was not an adequate enough explanation to account for all phenomena. The nineteenth century German mathematician Bernard Riemann (1826-1866) was one of the first to rebel from the simple world of Euclidean geometry, in which life and nature were seen as moving in patterns of grids and simple geometrical shapes. In 1854 he realized that the three-dimensional shape of the universe was bent in four-dimensional space into the shape of a hypersphere.[22] Riemann began to lecture about his discovery of a universe of many dimensions and in so doing inspired others to follow his lead. The laws he postulated led to what became known as non-Euclidean geometry, which was the starting point for Einstein's theories of relativity.[23]

One English mathematician emboldened by Riemann's theories, Charles Dodgson (1832-1898), wrote a series of popular books that integrated Riemann's findings and captivated the public's imagination in the bargain. Dodgson wrote them ostensibly as children's books and used his niece Alice as the main character of the stories. Using the pseudonym Lewis Carroll, his books *Alice in Wonderland* and *Through the Looking Glass* were stories of visits to worlds of alternative forms of logic and convention that defied common sense—in other words, the world of higher dimensions and aperspectivalism.[24]

The integral-aperspectival age may have ushered in a new consciousness, as Gebser and many others have suggested. In 1929 during the early stages of this new worldview, Leo Frobenius wrote:

> We are concerned no longer with cultural inflections, but with a passage from one culture stage to another. In all previous ages, only restricted portions of the surface of the earth were known. Men looked out from the narrowest, upon a somewhat larger neighborhood, and beyond that, a great unknown. They were all, so to say, insular: bound in. Whereas our view is confined no longer to a spot of space on the surface of this earth. It surveys the whole of the planet. And this fact, this lack of horizon, is something new.[25]

Frobenius considered this emerging new epoch the Global or World Culture. If he is right, it is a consciousness that is still emerging and will continue to evolve over the years to come. If so, it will have a bearing on the human potential and healing capacities for human beings.

Chapter Notes

1. Thomas, quoted in Radin, Dean. *The Conscious Universe*. San Francisco: HarperSanFrancisco, 1997: 290.

2. Feynman, quoted in Wilczek, Frank. "The end of physics?" *Discover*. 14, no. 3 (March 1993): 32.

3. Wilczek, "The end of physics?" p. 32.

4. Chan, Wing-Tsit. *A Source Book in Chinese Philosophy*. Princeton: Princeton University Press, 1963.

5. Kothari, D. S. "Complementarity principle and syadvada." In A.P. French and J.P. Kennedy (eds.). *Niels Bohr*. Cambridge, MA: Harvard University Press, 1985: 325.

6. Wilber, Ken. *Integral Psychology*. Boston: Shambhala Publications, 2000: 2.

7. Wilber, Ken. *The Eye of Spirit*. Boston: Shambhala Publications, 1997: x.

8. Wilber, Ken. "How big is our umbrella." *Noetic Sciences Review Online Archives*. Winter 1996. www.noetic.org/ions/archivelisting_frame.asp?ID=291.

9. Wilber, Ken. *Sex, Ecology, Spirituality*. Boston: Shambhala Publications, 1995: 191.

10. Rohmann, Chris. *A World of Ideas*. New York: Ballantine Books, 1999: 171.

11. Aurobindo, quoted in Dalal, A.S. *A Greater Psychology: An Introduction to the Psychological Thought of Sri Aurobindo*. New York: Tarcher/Putnam, 2001: 2.

12. Aurobindo, Sri. *The Life Divine*. Pondicherry, India: Sri Aurobindo Ashram Trust, 1990: 397-398.

13. Winston, Michael R. "Aurobindo Ghose and world reconstruction." *Journal of Religious Thought*. 51, no. 1 (Summer/Fall 1994): 17.

14. Aurobindo, Sri. *Essays on the Gita*. New York: E.P. Dutton and Co, 1950: 268.

15. Winston, "Aurobindo Ghose and world reconstruction," p. 14.

16. Gebser, Jean. *The Ever-Present Origin*. Translated by Noel Barstad and Algis Mickunas. Athens, Ohio: Ohio University Press, 1985.

17. Ibid, p. 3.

18. Ibid, p. 2.

19. Ibid.

20. Wilber, Ken. *The Marriage of Sense and Soul*. New York: Random House, 1998:131.

21. Blake, in Ostriker, Alicia (ed.). *William Blake: The Complete Poems*. New York:Penguin, 1977.

22. Rucker, Rudy. *Infinity and the Mind*. Princeton: Princeton University Press, 1995:17.

23. Gebser, in Saher, P.J. *Eastern Wisdom and Western Thought: A Comparative Study in the Modern Philosophy of Religion*. London: George Allen and Unwin, Ltd., 1969: 2.

24. Kaku, Michio. *Hyperspace*. New York: Oxford University Press, 1994: 22.

25. Frobenius, in Wilber, *Sex, Ecology, Spirituality*, p. 190.

Ten

Stages of Development

Although the integral approach is a multiple-perspectives view, in which no perspective is final and all perspectives interrelate, there must be a way to determine if one perspective has more value than another. In other words, is there a hierarchy of ideas that can distinguish between qualities of concepts and be able to put all of these concepts within a greater context? If there is no mechanism for distinguishing, then it is possible to run into what is known as "aperspectival madness"—the belief that no belief is any better than any other.[1]

As previously discussed, Sri Aurobindo felt that all life was a continuum and argued that within this continuum we progress from partial truth to a more complete truth. Nature also works within a continuum: atoms become molecules, which become cells, which become tissues, which become organisms. In complexity theory autopoiesis has shown that the components of a system work together to make and remake the system. Complexity theory has also shown that life is a web of integrated components that share information and use it to self-organize, develop, and evolve. And when the time is ripe, evolution creates transformations into new, emergent properties.

EVOLUTION AND SELF-ORGANIZATION

It would seem, then, that there is a continuum or hierarchy in nature. The process of evolution has demonstrated that nature has hierarchical properties and goes through stages of development. Out of the conditions created by evolution in the physical realm came the conditions that allowed for biological evolution to occur; and out of the conditions that created biological evolution, came the conditions that allowed for human beings and other species to develop; and out of these conditions came the conditions for the evolution of the mind to occur.

From a strict Darwinian sense, evolution does not sufficiently explain the possible emergence of new properties. Darwin saw evolution as natural selection amidst the randomness of genetic mutations. He felt chance mutation leads to genetic alterations. Although the vast majority of them are maladaptive, a few contribute to a greater (or at least different) capacity for adaptation and survival, and these mutations are thus selected and genetically carried forward in the gene pool. However, scientists now almost universally recognize that although natural selection can account quite well for microevolution (or variation within a given range of possibilities), it doesn't account for macroevolution, or the emergence of new properties.[2]

Furthermore, the new sciences have shown that this is a participatory universe, one in which subject and object interact in a way that helps construct and give meaning to life. Neurobiologist Francisco Varela, who was a longtime student of the complexity sciences, displayed, through his work, that life is based on the interaction between subject and object. He called this the enactive view of knowing the world and felt that language and the nervous system constantly construct a person's environment, putting it in a constant state of flux and evolution. Varela wrote, "We lay it down as we walk on its path."[3]

It may therefore be that evolution has a basis in this enactive view in the subject-object relationship. Organisms may evolve both because of an internal drive and because of an interaction with nature; and both of these may be linked to the self-organizing drive that all living systems have to constantly evolve and transform.

The compulsion of living systems to self-organize may have roots that go as deep as quantum reality. Perhaps the modus operandi for self-organization is based on a formula that is inclusive of the nonlocal nature of the universe; the native communication that takes place in the quantum realm among wave-particles; and the information that is shared between the quantum and classical realms. Contrary to Darwin's contention/claim that evolution was the random meanderings of nature, evolution may be an intrinsic movement towards emergence that is inherent in nature.

A growing number of people subscribe to this integral view, including the developmental psychologist Robert Kegan, who says:

> You could posit that there is a drive within living forms, including humans, to shape reality and create ever more satisfactory connections or relationships to the universe...What's the source of this drive? Now you are really asking a religious question about what is the nature of life itself, or energy itself, this intelligent energy that forms and re-forms itself. At another level, I could just as happily answer the question by saying God. God moves all this—where God is the name of the ceaseless, restless, creative flow of energy in the universe...This intelligent energy, this restless, creative flow that we can follow within any one single life, is actually something in which the universe as a whole participates. It's really not one energy that's running through the whole thing. It's not something we share, so much as it is something that shares us.[4]

Kegan's perspective on evolution has spiritual implications. At its core the integral worldview is a spiritual one in that it believes there is a drive that underpins all life and that this drive is an evolutionary one that has a spiritual nature. This belief is not unlike what many spiritual and wisdom traditions have maintained—that there is what is known as a Great Chain of Being.

The belief of a Great Chain of Being was predicated on seeing reality as having a purpose, driven by a consciousness, or a spirit, and that this drive was one continuous and interrelated manifestation of spirit. This Great Chain reaches in a perfectly unbroken or uninterrupted fashion from matter to life to mind to soul to spirit.[5] The theory of the Great Chain coalesces with the emergent theory of evolution, whereby life first evolved in the physical realm, known as the physiosphere, then in the biological realm, known as the biosphere, and more recently in the mental realm, known as the noosphere. The Great Chain theorists believe the process of evolution will proceed beyond the noosphere into the evolutionary emergence of the soul and spiritual realms, known as the theosphere.[6]

An emergence of realms beyond the noosphere is something science of and by itself is not capable of accounting for. A pure physical description of the universe, such as science gives, can never be a complete description of the universe. Stephen Hawking believes that only when physics unravels the mysteries of the universe will the mind of God be known.[7] Yet as physicist Frank Wilczek stated earlier, the only mind that science may ever know is that of slugs.[8] To truly know what mind, consciousness, and spirit are may entail having to wait until the emergent properties of these realms unfold and become manifest.

A DIRECTION TO THE UNIVERSE

It was Aristotle and the ancient Greeks who first conceived that the universe might have a greater purpose, what they called a teleology. According to Aristotle, it was incomprehensible that the universe emerged out of darkness or chaos. He felt the purpose, beauty, and order of the world was a fact, borne of what was called "a hierarchy of beings."[9] This hierarchy was based on a purpose of all beings—to fulfill their inherent potential. The acorn grows into an oak tree, the child into an adult. Form is the innate content of something, developed to its fullest potential either through entelechy, the actualization of its native potential, or through another's agency. Tracing efficient cause back to its source, Aristotle concluded that there must be a Prime Mover, an "uncaused cause" that is pure form and wholly actualized.[10]

The ancient Greek philosophers used the term *kosmos*, which means the patterned whole of all existence, a matrix that includes the physical, emotional, mental, and spiritual realms. They believed that the evolution of people's lives goes through general stages that are universally shared. Furthermore, they felt this matrix is omnipresent not just in the lives of the individual, but in the lives of the community and society and in the ebb and flow of nature and the external, objective, physical world.

A belief in a teleology, or purposiveness, did not mean the universe had a set preordained purpose or path, or that there was an omnipotent power pulling strings. Instead, their teleological explanation for the universe meant there was an orientation and direction to the universe, albeit a meandering one. Although most who have subscribed or currently subscribe to a teleological perspective see the direction of the universe in a positive light and see the dawning of a new age of consciousness approaching, there are no guarantees for man's successful continuation in the universe. Human beings are just as capable of blowing themselves up as they are of cultivating new emergent properties. For humans to progress in a positive direction may demand the further development of human potential and the cultivation of emergent properties.

The integral thinkers are those who most readily accept this developmental model of the universe. They envision the developing universe in relation to something ultimate, eternal, or everlasting.[11] According to one of his biographers, Gustav Fechner (1801-1887), one of the founders of modern psychology, was one such person. Fechner maintained that the whole universe is spiritual in character, the phenomenal world of physics being merely the external manifestation of this spiritual reality. Atoms are only the simplest elements in a spiritual hierarchy leading up to God. Each level of this hierarchy includes all those levels beneath it, so that God contains the totality of spirits. Consciousness is an essential feature of all that exists. The evidences of soul are the systematic coherence and conformity to law exhibited in the behavior of organic wholes. Fechner regarded the earth, "our mother," as such an organic besouled whole.[12]

However, as the field of psychology progressed, it did not follow Fechner's lead. Instead of looking at the universe as essentially spiritual in nature, spirituality was seen as something pathological. Freud called it "infantile helplessness" and a "regression to primary narcissism."[13] A contemporary psychiatrist, Robert Turner of the University of California at San Francisco's School of Medicine, has stated that "There's been a long-standing practice for psychiatry to pathologize or ignore religious experience."[14] Although Carl Jung returned spirituality to the psychology arena, it was not a developmental approach, as Fechner's was. Thus, the developmental mantle passed onto integral thinkers from fields other than psychology.

Developmentalists are in general agreement that there is an evolutionary direction to the universe, proceeding through an evolution of consciousness and existence that advances through a series of eight to twelve universal stages. This direction is not only seen in human beings, but it is intrinsic in every living system from subatomic particles, atoms, molecules, and cells to planets, stars, and universes. This intrinsic quality has been observed in quantum mechanics and complexity theory, but from a scientific perspective it is not fully understood. An integral theory has mapped this understanding out the best, and because an integral theory is capable of seamlessly integrating science and spirituality, it is probably the most complete theory of everything.

While addressing a conference of scientists, the Dalai Lama once said that if he were not a monk, he would have liked to have been an engineer.[15] This is an integral statement—what better person to utter such a remark than a man who understands how science and spirituality are two aspects of the same reality?

STAGES OF DEVELOPMENT

Another psychologist who found his way to developmentalism and an integral approach was Clare W. Graves (1914-1986). Graves was a professor at Union College in Schenectady, NY, and in the early 1950s he was dissatisfied with psychology and was ready to leave the field because he considered the field to be "in such a mess."[16] There were so many competing theories, and he could not tell his students which was right. He decided to embark on a major research project and study human nature. He was interested in knowing why people think the way they do, why they are different, and why some change while others do not. His research moved him in the direction of developmentalism. He proposed that the "psychology of the mature human being is an unfolding, emergent, oscillating spiraling process marked by progressive subordination of older, lower-order behavior systems to newer, higher-order systems as man's existential problems change."[17] His research supported the same conclusion that other developmentalists and integral thinkers had arrived at:

> My data supported the conclusion that human nature is such that modes of being can ebb and flow. New ones can replace old ones, yet the old ones don't disappear. They still exist within us. Furthermore, there are potentially new modes of being on the horizon that we have not experienced...Human existence contains numerous, probably infinite, modes of being, precisely rooted in

the multifold potentiality of mankind's hierarchically structured brain. What you have encountered is simply evidence of the emergence of different modes of being in people and, under certain conditions, changes to other levels of existence.[18]

Like all developmentalists, Graves believed human behavior went through universal stages of being with each successive level allowing for a more mature level of thinking. He mapped out a number of these stages, and after he passed away, his students Don Beck and Chris Cowan elaborated on Graves' findings in a system they call Spiral Dynamics, which postulates a hierarchy of eight different levels of existence. They based Spiral Dynamics on the following assumption:

We have adaptive intelligences, "complex, adaptive, contextual intelligences," which develop in response to our life circumstances and challenges—what Spiral Dynamics calls Life Conditions. What we're always focusing on are the causative dynamics created by the Life Conditions and then the kinds of coping mechanisms and collective intelligences that are forged in response to those conditions. These collective intelligences are what we call memes.[19]

According to Beck and Cowan, there are eight levels, or stages, of existence that the Spiral Dynamics developmental model incorporates.[20]

1. Beige: Archaic-Instinctual. The level of basic survival; food, water, warmth, sex, and safety have priority. Uses habits and instincts just to survive. Distinct self is barely awakened or sustained. Forms into survival bands to perpetuate life. Examples: First human societies, newborn infants, senile elderly, late-stage Alzheimer's victims, mentally ill street people, starving masses, shell shock. Approximately 0.1 percent of the adult population.

2. Purple: Magical-Animistic. Thinking is animistic; magical spirits, good and bad, swarm the earth leav-

ing blessings, curses, and spells which determine events. Forms into ethnic tribes. The spirits exist in ancestors and bond the tribe. Kinship and lineage establish political links. Examples: Belief in voodoo-like curses, blood oaths, ancient grudges, good-luck charms, family rituals, magical ethnic beliefs and superstitions; strong in third-world settings, gangs, and athletic teams, and corporate "tribes." Approximately 10 percent of the population.

3.   Red: Power Gods. First emergence of a self distinct from the tribe; powerful, impulsive, egocentric, heroic. Magical-mythic spirits, dragons, beings, forces to be reckoned with, both good and bad. Feudal lords protect underlings in exchange for obedience and labor. The basis of feudal empires—power and glory. The world is a jungle full of threats and predators. Conquers, outfoxes, and dominates; enjoys self to the beasts, and powerful people. Archetypal gods and goddesses, powerful fullest without regret or remorse; be here now. Examples: The "terrible twos," rebellious youth, frontier mentalities, feudal kingdoms, epic heroes, James Bond villains, gang leaders, soldiers of fortune, New-Age narcissism, wild rock stars, Attila the Hun, Lord of the Flies. Approximately 20 percent of the population.

4.   Blue: Mythic Order. Life has meaning, direction, and purpose, with outcomes determined by an all-power-ful Other or Order. This righteous Order enforces a code of conduct based on absolutist and unvarying principles of "right" and "wrong." Violating the code or rules has severe, perhaps everlasting repercussions. Following the code yields rewards for the faithful. Basis of ancient nations. Rigid social hierarchies; paternalistic; one right way and only one right way to think about everything. Law and order; impulsivity controlled through guilt; concrete-literal and fun-

damentalist belief; obedience to the rule of Order; strongly conventional and conformist. Often religious or mythic, but can be secular or atheistic Order or Mission. Examples: Puritan America, Confucian China, Dickensian England, Singapore discipline, totalitarianism, codes of chivalry and honor, charitable good deeds, religious fundamentalism, Boy and Girl Scouts, moral majority, patriotism. Approximately 40 percent of the population.

5.   Orange: Scientific Achievement. At this level, the self "escapes" from the "herd mentality" of blue and seeks truth and meaning in individualistic terms— hypothetico–deductive, experimental, objective, mechanistic, operational— "scientific" in the typical sense. The world is a rational and well-oiled machine with natural laws that can be learned, mastered, and manipulated for one's own purposes. Highly achieve-ment-oriented, especially towards materialistic gains. The laws of science rule politics, the economy, and human events. The world is a chessboard on which games are played as winners gain preeminence and perks over losers. Marketplace alliances; manipulate earth's resources for one's strategic gains. Basis of corporate states. Examples: The Enlightenment, Ayn Rand's *Atlas Shrugged*, Wall Street, emerging middle classes around the world, cosmetics industry, trophy hunting, colonialism, the Cold War, fashion industry, materialism, secular humanism, liberal self-interest, Approximately 30 percent of the population.

6.   Green: The Sensitive Self. Communitarian, human bonding, ecological sensitivity, networking. The human spirit must be freed from greed, dogma, and divisiveness; feelings and caring supercede cold rationality; cherishing of the earth, Gaia, life. Against hierarchy; establishes lateral bonding and linking. Permeable self, relational self, group intermeshing.

Emphasis on dialogue, relationships. Basis of value communities (i.e., freely chosen affiliations based on shared sentiments). Reaches decisions through reconciliation and consensus. Refresh spirituality, bring harmony, enrich human potential. Strongly egalitarian, antihierarchy, pluralistic values, social construction of reality, diversity, multiculturalism, relativistic value systems; this worldview is often called pluralistic relativism. Subjective, nonlinear thinking; shows a greater degree of affective warmth, sensitivity and caring, for earth and all its inhabitants. Examples: Deep ecology, postmodernism, Netherlands idealism, Rogerian counseling, Canadian health care, humanistic psychology, liberation theology, cooperative inquiry, World Council of Churches, Greenpeace, animal rights, ecofeminism, post-colonialism, Foucault-Derrida, politically correct, diversity movements, human rights issues, ecopsychology. Approximately 10 percent of the population.

7.   Yellow: Integrative. Life is a kaleidoscope of natural hierarchies, systems, and forms. Flexibility, spontaneity, and functionality have the highest priority. Differences and pluralities can be integrated into interdependent, natural flows. Egalitarianism is complemented with natural degrees of ranking and excellence. Knowledge and competency should supercede power, status, or group sensitivity. The prevailing world order is the result of the existence of different levels of reality and the inevitable patterns of movement up and down the dynamic spiral. Good governance facilitates the emergence of entities through the levels of increasing complexity (nested hierarchy). Approximately 1 percent of the population.

8. Turquoise: Holistic. Universal holistic system, waves of integrative energies; unites feeling with knowledge; multiple levels interwoven into one conscious system. Universal order, but in a living, conscious fashion, not based on external rules (blue) or group bonds (green). A grand unification, or a theory of everything is possible, in theory and in actuality. Sometimes involves the emergence of a new spirituality as a meshwork of all existence. Turquoise thinking uses the entire spiral, all of the levels; sees multiple levels of interaction; detects harmonics, the mystical forces, and the pervasive flow-states that permeate any organization. Approximately 0.1 percent of the population.

Within the Spiral Dynamics model, as with all developmental models, each successive level supercedes the previous level in a manner that transcends and includes all former levels. "When a new worldview emerges, the previously awakened memes do not disappear," explains Beck. "Rather, they remain subsumed in the total flow and not only add texture to the more complex ways of living, but remain 'on call' in case the problems that first awakened them to service reappear. So, there are systems within us, miniature worldviews, each of which is calibrated for different problems of existence. Like the Russian dolls, there are systems within systems within systems within systems."[21]

Beck and Cowan's model is one among many developmental models, most of which concur on the general design: awareness and consciousness advancing and evolving through a series of unfolding stages, each higher level transcending and including the previous level. The early stages tend to be prerational and prepersonal; the middle stages rational and personal; and the higher stages transpersonal and transrational. In Beck and Cowan's model, the first six stages are prerational and rational, and are what they call First Tier levels; the latter two stages are transrational and are called Second Tier levels.

One of the first scientists to look at life from a developmental perspective was James Mark Baldwin (1861-1934), a psychologist whose works greatly influenced Jean Piaget and many other developmentalists.

Baldwin came to see consciousness as developing through a half-dozen distinct stages or levels of consciousness. He called the early stages the prelogical, quasilogical, and logical. Baldwin continued by mapping out areas that he felt went beyond the purely logical: the extralogical, and finally, to what he felt was the endstage, the hyperlogical. He considered this stage to be the zenith of human experience, a state of consciousness that "is a form of contemplation…in which the immediacy of experience constantly seeks to reestablish itself."

> In the highest form of such contemplation, a form which comes to itself as genuine and profound aesthetic experience, we find a synthesis of motives, a mode in which the strands of the earlier and diverging dualism are merged and fused…an experience whose essential character is just its unity of comprehension, [wherein] consciousness has its completest and most direct and final apprehension of what reality is and means.[22]

Some developmentalists have speculated there are stages beyond what have been mapped, realms in which cosmic consciousness and spiritual illumination exist.[23] Sri Aurobindo called these states the Supermind, or the supramental state, and believed they were high and powerful levels of consciousness that held the key to humanity's human and evolutionary potential.[24] If such realms do exist, mortals visit them only rarely. Cowan and Beck estimate that only 1.1 percent of the world's population exist at the seventh and eighth levels, yellow and turquoise. If there are levels beyond yellow and turquoise, such as the realms postulated by Sri Aurobindo, it can only be speculated what percentage resides there, but it would obviously have to be considerably less than 1.1 percent. These levels of existence can be called third tier levels.

The course of evolution runs from a lesser to a greater level, or from a lesser to a greater awareness. Like all of nature, this course does not occur linearly. As nature meanders and flows nonlinearly, so does evolution. Just as humanity is capable of evolving at some future time to levels of consciousness that can only presently be imagined, humanity is also capable of blowing itself up to smithereens. Humanity does not passively sit around and wait for its destiny to unfold. As discussed earlier, it is an enactive path, and it is laid down as humans walk the path. In other words, it is up to mankind to choose what direction humanity takes.

Chapter Notes:

1. Wilber, Ken. *Integral Psychology*. Boston: Shambhala Publications, 2000: 170.

2. Varela, Francisco, Evan Thompson and Eleanor Rosch. *The Embodied Mind*. Cambridge, MA: MIT Press, 1993.

3. Varela, quoted in Schlitz, Marilyn. "Researcher Profile: Francisco J. Varela." *Institute of Noetic Sciences Archives*, 1998: 1.

4. Kegan, Robert. "Epistemology, fourth order consciousness, and the subject-object relationship or...How the self evolves." Interview by Elizabeth Debold. *What is Enlightenment?* No. 22 (Fall/Winter 2002): 152.

5. Lovejoy, Arthur. *The Great Chain of Being*. Cambridge, MA: Harvard University Press, 1936.

6. Ibid.

7. Hawking, Stephen. *A Brief History of Time*. New York: Bantam, 1988.

8. Wilczek, Frank. "The end of physics?" *Discover*. 14, no. 3 (March 1993): 32.

9. Jaspers, Karl. *The Great Philosophers*. New York: Harcourt Brace and Co, 1981:205-06.

10. Rohmann, Chris. *A World of Ideas*. New York: Ballantine Books, 1999: 27.

11. Redfield, James, Michael Murphy and Sylvia Timbers. *God and the Evolving Universe*. New York: Jeremy P. Tarcher, 2002: 57.

12. Zweig, A. "Gustav Theodor Fechner." In Paul Edwards. *The Encyclopedia of Philosophy, Vol. 3*. New York: Macmillan, 1967: 181.

13. Wallis, Claudia. "Faith and healing." *Time*. 147, no. 26 (June 24, 1996): 59.

14. Stone, Elizabeth. "Is there a God? Am I crazy?" *Elle*. 10, no. 4 (Dec. 1994): 60.

15. Scheinin, Richard. "Dalai Lama explores ties that bind science and religion." *Tribune News Service*. (April 25, 1994).

16. Beck, Don and Chris Cowan. *Spiral Dynamics: Mastering Values, Leadership, and Change*. Malden, MA: Blackwell Publishers, 1996: 39.

17. Graves, quoted in Beck and Cowan, *Spiral Dynamics: Mastering Values, Leadership, and Change*, p. 28.

18. Ibid, p. 39.

19. Beck, Don. "The never-ending upward quest: The practical and spiritual wisdom of spiral dynamics." Interview by Jessica Roemischer. *What is Enlightenment?* No. 22 (Fall/Winter 2002): 110.

20. Wilber, Ken. *A Theory of Everything*. Boston: Shambhala Publications, 2000: 9-13.

21. Beck, "The never-ending upward quest: The practical and spiritual wisdom of spiral dynamics," p. 111.

22. Wilber, Ken. *Integral Psychology*. Boston: Shambhala Publications, 2000: 79-80.

23. Kimura, Yasuhiko. "A philosopher of change." An interview by Carter Phipps. *What is Enlightenment?* No. 22 (Fall/Winter 2002): 28.

24. Hamilton, Craig. "Why Sri Aurobindo is cool." *What is Enlightenment?* No. 21 (Spring/Summer 2002): 66-77, 153.

Eleven

Toward a Quantum-Integral Medicine

The integral perspective, which understands all aspects of life to be interconnected, can also view one specific discipline, such as medicine, in the same way. An integral approach would allow for the integration of all medicine—western biomedicine, Chinese medicine and other systems of medicine, like Ayurveda and Homeopathy, energy medicine, mind-body medicine, biopsychosocial medicine, spiritual healing, and other forms of healing. The sciences that would form the foundation for this type of approach would be quantum theory and chaos and complexity theories, since it is these sciences that give the most accurate physical description of the nature of life.

If a worldview encompassing these new perspectives were applied to the field of medicine, medicine could become more cost-effective, proficient, and relevant to the needs and desires of people. It could also assist in helping people tap into the wellspring of innate healing capabilities that reside within and allow people to utilize more of their human potential. This type of approach could be called Quantum-Integral Medicine.

The quantum view states that life emanates as infinite possibility waves from a great void, the quantum vacuum, and it is all pervasive throughout the universe. It is postulated that in the everyday world, a silent pulse connects ordinary reality with this quantum reality, and through quantum creativity, or the shifting of the mind, the two worlds can be connected.

The integral view states that all perspectives interrelate and emanate from a spiritual source, a consciousness or mind, which is believed to exist in both the objective and subjective domains. Furthermore, it is believed that a graded spectrum, a hierarchy, needs to be traversed in order to fully access and understand this Source. This hierarchy is the evolution in consciousness from prerational to rational to transrational.

Quantum theory gives a scientific explanation to the fields of energy and nonlocal healing approaches, modalities that are part of what the National Center for Complementary and Alternative Medicine calls "frontier medicine." Integral theory complements and adds more depth to quantum theory by suggesting that energy has a consciousness and intelligence and a direction, an evolution, a teleology, towards a greater whole. Integral theory also shows that this direction's movement and trajectory is one of complexity and nonlinear dynamics. Within that framework, a self-organizing principle occurs that moves life towards greater awareness and greater evolutionary capability.

The umbrella of Quantum-Integral Medicine is large enough to encompass the varied range of healing modalities from western medicine to biopsychosocial medicine, mind-body medicine, and nonlocal healing, or, as Larry Dossey has categorized all these modalities, Eras I, II, and III of medicine.[1] It can create an umbrella large enough to include all of medicine within a continuum, a continuum that progresses, as Sri Aurobindo has argued, from a partial truth to a more complete truth. This continuum is the direction that evolution and self-organization take from lesser to greater awareness.

The worldview biomedicine generally operates from is only a partial truth in that it is a linear deterministic model that tends to dismiss as anomalies things it can't explain. A more complete truth would recognize that organisms are dynamic and continually evolve and self-organize. This drive which can be seen occurring within the body, finds its manifestation in the innate healing capabilities of people. This innate healing force is something Norman Cousins saw as a "grand orchestration" of all the forces that move a person from sickness to health.[2]

Biomedicine tends to be a physical medicine, believing essentially in the physical causes of illness[3] and thereby prescribing physical interventions—surgery, drugs, and behavioral modification. While this has an important place, the human condition is complex and sophisticated, and often the problem is not purely physical in origin. This is why traditional healers have believed what Ali Pul, the physician of traditional Arabic medicine quoted earlier, said: "The medicine of the soul is the medicine of the body."[4]

Biomedicine does not have a good track record with chronic ailments because these are more complicated, diverse, and unpredictable, and do not fit in with biomedicine's more linear approach that requires predictable patterns following set rules. For this reason biomedicine has problems with viruses, even those as commonplace as the common cold, because there is much turbulence and complexity with chronic illness and viruses. In its desire to maintain a linear course, biomedicine desires to tame nature's impulse to be diverse and complex. In effect, biomedicine is still living by Francis Bacon's scientific philosophy of disciplining and torturing nature. But as biophysicist Beverly Rubik says, "Nature is not something we should be fighting against and feeling alienated from, but it's very much a part of who we are."[5]

Instead of seeing the dynamics of the human body as a microcosm of nature's complex movements and attempting to work in a cooperative and synergistic manner with the body, biomedicine prefers to cajole, coerce, and assault nature, so that it will do what biomedicine wants. Although drugs and surgery are inappropriate for many chronic illnesses, that is precisely what biomedicine will mandate. Complications from drugs and surgery are the reasons for one third of patients being admitted to critical care units.[6] According to Larry Dossey, "In any other sphere of modern life, this situation would rank as a national scandal. Modern medicine would win the death derby every time by a landslide."[7]

THE INNATE HEALING FORCE

Quantum-Integral Medicine would view the innate healing force as a core component of healing, and as such, it would see nature playing a central role in the healing process. Nature would be cultivated and encouraged, not suppressed and controlled. It would be understood that nature follows a complex path and moves in a self-organizing manner to greater evolutionary wholeness. It would also be understood that nature has a spiritual drive and the encouragement of this drive can inspire the innate healing force every person has within.

Yet, it is not an either/or scenario, in which a person must choose either biomedicine or an alternative. Choosing biomedicine need not negate the cultivation of the innate healing force. The current popularity nowadays of Integrative Medicine has made combination therapies more pervasive and accepted. From a Quantum-Integral Medicine perspective, the most important element, first and foremost, is the cultivation of the spiritual healing force and, secondarily, the therapy or therapies involved.

As a young pediatrician, Rachel Naomi Remen once had as a patient a twelve-year-old girl with Hodgkin's disease, a cancer of the lymph nodes, who had come from New York City for radiation treatment at the Stanford linear accelerator. Her father, an Orthodox rabbi, was deeply traditional and obeyed all the rituals and laws. For the Orthodox, the holiest day of the year is Yom Kippur, the day of atonement for sins committed. On this day, among other things, money is not handled, the skins of animals and even leather shoes are not worn, and a person does not ride in cars or use electricity for any purpose. Shoshana's eighth treatment fell on Yom Kippur. The accelerator was too far for this ill young girl to reach by walking and her father came to see Remen to discuss this. He explained the importance of the meticulous observance of Yom Kippur. He proposed skipping the treatment.

"No," Remen told the father, "The timing of these treatments is critical to Shoshana's recovery." Angrily he told Remen that she was not to go, because "God's laws superseded any human law." Remen was horrified, and replied back, "Are you telling me that God's law is more important than your child's treatment? What sort of God would ask this?" Offended, the father quoted the story of Abraham and Isaac and then left the office saying that he would refer the matter to a higher authority, the rabbi in New York City who headed his sect of Orthodox Judaism.

On the morning of Yom Kippur, Shoshana was sitting in her usual place in the waiting room, on time. With her were her mother *and* her father. "I am surprised to see you here, Rabbi," Remen said. "What did the rabbi in New York say?" Subdued, he told her that he had written to describe the situation and his Rabbi, the Great Teacher himself, had called him. He had told him to order a taxi to come to his home on the morning of Yom Kippur. When the taxi arrived, Shoshana was to ride to her treatment and he was to accompany her.

When he protested riding in a car on Yom Kippur, his Rabbi had insisted he accompany his daughter. "Why is this?" Remen asked. In a soft voice he said that his Rabbi, the Great Teacher, had insisted that he accompany his daughter so that she would know that even the most pious and upright man in her life, her father, may ride on the holiest days for the purpose of preserving life. He said that it was important that Shoshana not feel separated from God by this breaking of the law. Such a feeling might interfere with her healing.[8]

His Rabbi was teaching the father that his support for his daughter would strengthen her bond with God and thereby strengthen her innate healing capabilities. It is most important in the process of healing to cultivate the healing force within, and the Great Teacher understood this dynamic.

The Greek physician Galen (129-199) noted, "He cures most successfully in whom the people have the most confidence."[9] This confidence can occur for many reasons. It may be an aspect of a resonance that occurs between healer and patient. In a manner not fully understood, a mind-body mechanism that occurs in the healing process triggers an innate healing force within the person to be healed.

Psychologist Lawrence LeShan, one of the pioneers of mind-body medicine, wrote about a man he knew who asked him to do a distance healing for an extremely painful condition requiring immediate and intensive surgery. "I promised to do the healing that night, and the next morning when he awoke a 'miraculous cure' had occurred." The medical specialist was astounded and offered to send him pre- and post- healing X-rays and to sponsor publication in a scientific journal. It would have been the psychic healing case of the century except for one small detail, writes LeShan. "In the press of overwork, I had forgotten to do the healing! If I had only remembered, it would have been a famous demonstration of what can be accomplished by this method."[10]

Placebos and the Innate Healing Force

Some would deride this as purely a placebo effect and interpret it as the man wanting to become better, and so he did. However, perhaps this so-called placebo effect is due to a mechanism that is related to the innate healing force. Cardiologist Herbert Benson, another pioneer of mind-body medicine, has done extensive research on the placebo effect and believes this to be the case.

His research has shown that the placebo effect yields beneficial clinical results in 60-90% of diseases that include angina pectoris, bronchial asthma, herpes simplex, and duodenal ulcer. He believes the placebo effect depends on the positive beliefs and expectations on the part of the patient, positive beliefs and expectations on the part of the physician or health care professional, and a good relationship between the two parties. Ultimately, Benson thinks, the placebo effect triggers memories in the central nervous system of what good health is, leading to events that result in feelings of well-being. Benson has coined the phrase "remembered wellness" to explain this effect.[11]

If there is such a thing as remembered wellness, it may be a constituent of the evolutionary dynamics of self-organization towards greater levels of awareness. Perhaps remembered wellness is the highest and most ideal level of health, something that is ingrained in the body and something towards which the body is striving to evolve. If that is the case, and it is embedded in the body, something needs to trigger it. When something does trigger this intrinsic healing force that is the grand orchestration of all the forces that move a person from sickness to health, a person may be able to tap into their greater human potential and use it to get better.

THE TRIGGERING OF THE INNATE HEALING FORCE

What is this mechanism that gets triggered? Is it something that another person triggers, or is it something people trigger by themselves? The answer is probably both. Here are two examples, one a trigger caused by a young girl, the other a trigger an individual caused himself.

A girl by the name of Audrey Santos, born December 19, 1983, and living in Worcester, MA, has been semicomatose ever since a swimming pool accident at age three. Since then, and up to the present day, she lays immobile in bed. Audrey is believed to have the power to heal by those who come to see her, though she does not seem to be aware of her surroundings. People have claimed to witness the appearance of stigmata on Audrey's hands and forehead, and have reported that in her home statues and paintings of saints have wept oil. Many who come to see her attest to her healing powers and her ability to bring them closer to God. On one anniversary of her accident, 8,000 people amassed in a football stadium to honor her.[12] A skeptic might look at this and dismiss it as mass hysteria. However, it may be either that the girl does have healing powers, which is catalyzing the triggering of the healing mechanism in people, or that people have invested her with powers and through their belief are triggering their own healing mechanisms. Either way, as her pediatrician has remarked, "Something different is going on here."[13]

Another example is the story of Arnold Lemerand of Southgate, Michigan. Mr. Lemerand had a heart attack in 1974. Six years later, at the age of 56, he was out for a walk when he found a five-year-old boy trapped under a cast iron pipe near a playground. Because of his heart attack, Mr. Lemerand had stopped lifting heavy objects. But without thinking he lifted the pipe and saved the child's life. As he was lifting it, he thought to himself that the pipe must weigh 300-400 pounds. It actually weighed 1800 pounds. Later, Mr. Lemerand, his grown sons, reporters, and police tried to lift the pipe, but they could not.[14] Apparently, in Mr. Lemerand's mind and body a mechanism was somehow triggered, which allowed him to pull off this superhuman feat.

The literature is filled with thousands of cases of people who have healed from serious ailments, many of whom were told they had no chance of living much longer and were left for dead.[15] Most have left the biomedical community scratching their heads in wonder, unsure of how a person could defy the odds and unable to give a biomedical explanation. One physician, pathologist Marco DeVries of St. Clara Hospital in Rotterdam, Netherlands, discussing one of his patients who healed herself of terminal cancer said, "If I really believed the pathologist in me, I wouldn't believe my eyes."[16] He was alluding to the fact that her tissue samples originally showed a fast-moving cancer. Yet years later she was alive, vital, and cancer-free.

When Dr. DeVries asked this patient what she was doing to reverse the cancer, she replied, "I said, it's just a feeling, something I know instinctively, from the inside. The emotions come up, and something happens in my body because of them, but I don't have words for it. It is just a big, big trust."[17]

One researcher, Charles Weinstock, M.D., who studied personality traits of people who go through profound healing experiences, found certain common factors in what he calls the Type M, or miracle, personality:

1)   Inner Change. Type M's go through an existential shift in the way they view themselves and their lives.

2)   Regression. This is a return to earlier states of function, in which a person can tap and relive their memories of when they felt happy and contented.

3)   Active Surrender. One patient exclaimed that his surrender was predicated on his understanding that life sometimes just is and the "universe doesn't arrange itself around my ego."

4)   Altered States. High hypnotizability, fantasy-proneness, dissociation, vivid dreams and perceptual alterations occur to some during their healing journey. As one person recalled, "Life became, well, psychedelic."

5)   Emotional Expression. Self-healers tend to emote easily and go through strong mood fluctuations. One personality study of self-healers found that they tend to have "more expressive and sometimes bizarre personalities."

6)   Social Change. Self-healers undergo a change in their interpersonal relationships. They realize that their relationship with others plays a role in their illness and they make either an intentional or accidental change for the better.[18]

The triggering mechanism that turns on the healing force might be analogous to the turning on of a light, as if the mechanism is a switch that is turning something on. One physician alluded to such a mechanism while talking about one of his patients, whose body was severely mangled in a car accident, but who managed to heal fully. "We tried the ordinary and the extraordinary as far as medicine goes, from mind-altering medication right up to hypnosis and acupuncture," he said, "but nothing worked. Whatever turned the switch and made him heal, it did it much more rapidly than conventional explanations allow."[19]

Evidence suggests that there is some sort of switching mechanism in the body, even if it is a figurative one. Something *is* triggered. Perhaps the mechanism is an aspect of a Godelian universe, of an open-ended universe in which the mind and body have to take a quantum leap to go beyond the system. The mind would very well do this in its quest to reach up to greater and greater heights in order to find a solution to a dilemma caused by the limits of rational thinking—in this case, the limits of biomedicine. It may also be an aspect of quantum thinking and quantum creativity, of the ability for the mind to tap into a greater whole where greater powers exist. Either way, what occurs is an aspect of metanoia, or shifting of the mind, that allows a person to tap into a greater current that underlies the body and mind.

The ability to understand and cultivate the greater human potential is a core component of Quantum-Integral Medicine. The ability to flip a switch in the mind is something everyone has the capacity to do. To do so requires tapping into a greater human potential and in the process going beyond the mental models that most people have embedded in their minds, models designed to maintain a status quo of a linear and deterministic universe.

Profound healings that people experience are often given the label of "spontaneous remission," or "spontaneous regression," as if unbeknownst to them, some mysterious force entered their body and washed away their sins. This belief, which is both naïve and reductionist, has many adherents in biomedicine because given their worldview, they lack any other logical explanation. However, as William Boyd points out in his book *The Spontaneous Regression of Cancer*, "The term spontaneous regression has a suggestion of something happening without a cause. That, of course, is absurd, for everything has a cause, apparent or inapparent."[20] Instead, it is probably closer to the way cancer survivor Debby Ogg put it. Discounting the term spontaneous, she said, "I worked my ass off for it."[21]

Understanding the mechanism that triggers the activation of the healing force is definitely a study well worth undertaking. "The possibility that medicine can learn to accomplish the same thing [so-called spontaneous or miracle healings] at will is surely within reach of imagining" remarked Lewis Thomas.[22] Larry Dossey has stated that to unravel the mysteries of miracles may take a Manhattan Project for Miracles, or a National Institute of the Miraculous.[23] To create such a project will take a new science of healing and human potential. This is one mission of a Quantum-Integral Medicine.

Chapter Notes

1. Dossey, Larry. *Reinventing Medicine*. New York: HarperCollins Publishers, 1999: 19.

2. Hirshberg, Caryle and Marc Barasch. *Remarkable Recovery*. New York: Riverhead Books, 1995: 18.

3. Lewit, K. "Changes in locomotor function, complementary medicine, and the general practitioner." *Journal of the Royal Society of Medicine*. 139, no. 12 (1994): 37.

4. Barasch, Marc. "A psychology of the miraculous." *Psychology Today*. 27, no. 2 (March/April 1994): 56.

5. Rubik, Beverly. "Exploring the Frontiers of Science." Interview by Russell DiCarlo. *HealthWorld Online*, 1996: 11. www.healthy.net/asp/templates/interview.asp?PageType=Interview&ID=297.

6. Shealy, C. Norman. *Sacred Healing*. Boston: Element Books, 1999: 38.

7. Dossey, in Shealy, *Sacred Healing*, p. 38.

8. Remen, Rachel Naomi. *Kitchen Table Wisdom: Stories That Heal*. New York: Riverhead Books, 1996: 277-78.

9. Galen, quoted in Schoofs, Mark. "Healing head trips." *The Village Voice*. 43, no. 19 (May 12, 1998): 22.

10. LeShan, Lawrence. *The Medium, the Mystic, and the Physicist*. New York: Ballantine Books, 1974: 125.

11. Benson, Herbert and Richard Friedman. "Harnessing the power of the placebo effect and renaming it remembered wellness." *Annual Review of Medicine*. 47 (1996): 193-99.

12. Hewitt, Bill and Tom Duffy. "In faith and hope." *People*. 50, no. 23 (Dec. 21, 1998): 146-48.

13. Ibid, p. 148.

14. "Names and FA." *The Boston Globe* (Nov. 1, 1980).

15. O'Regan, Brendan and Caryle Hirshberg. *Spontaneous Remission: An Annotated Bibliography*. Sausalito, CA: Institute of Noetic Sciences, 1993.

16. Hirshberg and Barasch, *Remarkable Recovery*, p. 162.

17. Ibid.

18. Weinstock, Charles. "Type M: Do you have a miracle personality?" *Psychology Today*. 27, no. 2 (March/April, 1994): 61-62.

19. Barasch, "A psychology of the miraculous," p. 60.

20. Boyd, William. *The Spontaneous Regression of Cancer*. New York: Charles C. Thomas, 1996: 8.

21. Barasch, "A psychology of the miraculous," p. 59.

22. Thomas, quoted in Dossey, Larry. "Canceled funerals: A look at miracle cures." *Alternative Therapies in Health and Medicine*. 4, no. 2 (March 1998): 118.

23. Dossey, "Canceled funerals: A look at miracle cures," p. 118.

Twelve

Towards a New Renaissance

What Is The Triggering Mechanism?

The late Japanese acupuncturist Yoshio Manaka has called the mechanism that triggers the activation of the healing force the "X-signal system."[1] He refers to it as a primitive signal system in the body that is biological, but does "not manifest through commonly known biological laws." He feels a cohesive theory of what the mechanism is has yet to be elucidated.

Many theorists are beginning to point the way towards a greater biological intelligence inherent within the body, but they are not yet fully capable of explaining the mechanism of what it is or how it operates. This era may be similar to the Quantum Stone Age of 1900-1925 discussed earlier, a period in which matter began to be seen in a new light, but no theories or laws existed yet to explain exactly what was being observed. In our present era, we are also witnesses to phenomena that cannot be dismissed outright or fully explained by current scientific laws.

Emergence

It may be that the mechanism is more than just a system within the body, which might be somewhat of a reductionist explanation. Instead, the answer might lie in the relationship between body, mind, and environment, and the capacity of life to create new and emergent behaviors.

Emergence is the movement to higher levels of order and sophistication in order to adapt to the environment. It used to be thought that when living systems changed into something new, following the course of what is called morphogenesis, there was some sort of master planner, or pacemaker, in the body directing the action. However, it is now understood that through the collective action of the living system a self-organization into a new pattern takes place, based on the requirements of the environment. There is no master planner, no pacemaker, directing the action. This is a web that has no weaver.

One example of this phenomenon is found in the complex patterns of ant colonies. Although some believe that the queen ant commands all other ants to build the colony, it is actually the other way around. The ants build the colony through collective action to protect the queen ant. Their entire behavior is predicated solely on finding safety for the queen so she can lay eggs.[2] The ants have no set way to build the colony; they will be as creative as possible as long as it achieves their goal. To create their colony, the ants build new architectural structures that adapt to the geography of the terrain. Thus, the ants are not ruled by a master planner who commands them to build the colony, but instead through collective action they self-organize into something new in order to meet their needs.

This process of creating anew is a key property of all open, living systems. This is emergence—life constantly reaching out to create new life or new properties in response to the variables presented. However, emergence is not a random happening; it does not occur unwittingly. Beneath the complexity there is always an order, a raison d'être. Perhaps the most important element of the underlying order is mind, or cognition. Research shows that living systems effect their environment, as well as being affected by them.[3]

According to the Santiago Theory of Cognition, as developed by Humberto Maturana and Francisco Varela, cognition, the process of knowing, is directly identified with the process of life. The organizing activity of living systems at all levels of life is mental activity, and the interactions of a living system with its environment are cognitive interactions. Maturana and Varela also developed the concept of autopoiesis, or self-making, and found a correlation between cognition and autopoiesis. A living system, they showed, responds to changes in its environment with autopoietic, structural changes. The structural changes that are created are not random occurrences; the living system selects which disturbances from the environment trigger the changes. In other words, there is a reason behind what a living system will notice and react to in its environment.[4]

Thus, there is a relationship between a living system and its environment, and mind is the mediator between the two. Cognition is the continual bringing forth of a world through the dynamic process of living and interacting; the interactions of a living system with its environment are cognitive interactions. This realization led Maturana and Varela to state "To live is to know."[5]

Emergence is a creative process because the creation of new properties, or structures, is based on the interaction of living system, mind, and environment, and because this interaction is a complex one, all kinds of options are possible, none of which are easily predictable. Certain frameworks are understood, however. For example, a man will never turn into a cockroach, as in a Franz Kafka story. Nonetheless, creative novelty within logical parameters is the hallmark of emergence.

Emergence may be the fundamental principle behind the ability to turn on the mechanism of the innate healing force. It may not be so much a biological mechanism within as much as a manifestation of a creative emergence that occurs from the interaction that takes place between body, mind, and environment, and its search for a remembered wellness. Creative emergence may be the trigger that turns on the mechanism of healing.

SPIRITUAL EMERGENCE

From an integral standpoint, the next level of emergence may be the emergence of the spiritual domain.[6] Spiritual emergence may turn out to be a defining feature of mankind as humans continue to evolve. If so, the ability to trigger the innate healing force may be one aspect of spiritual emergence and the furtherance of human potential another.

The first great emergence was the creation of earth from the physiosphere. The second great emergence was the creation of biological life. The third great emergence was the creation of mind.[7] It may very well be that if human beings continue to evolve, the next great emergence will be a spiritual one, the emergence of spirit. This view fits well with developmental theory, such as that of Spiral Dynamics, which contends that humans are evolving in consciousness and cognition, ultimately to levels barely known or imagined in this day and age. These upper levels would be considered spiritual ones. This also parallels the theory of the Great Chain of Being, which holds that life evolves from matter to body to mind to soul to spirit.

From an integral viewpoint, a spiritual emergence could herald another Renaissance, or Age of Enlightenment. This Age of Enlightenment would be similar to the one of a few hundreds years ago, in that it would bring forth a new way of thinking. But unlike the last one, this would not herald a blossoming of a more rational and perspectival way of seeing the world, but rather a more transrational and aperspectival way of seeing the world. This new Age of Enlightenment might follow more closely the definition of enlightenment as defined by various spiritual traditions.

EMERGENCE AND COMPLEXITY

Nonetheless, the emergence of more spiritual levels, or even of higher levels of mental capacity, will not occur by happenstance. It will take a dynamic in which the interaction of living systems, mind, and environment is pushed to the edge. Since emergence occurs in complex systems and complexity occurs when a system is at the edge of chaos, it stands to reason that emergence occurs when a system is at the edge of chaos and pushed to the brink. In evolution when a living system is pushed to the brink, it reaches the point at which it either continues to do things in the old manner and possibly face extinction, or it facilitates emergence and the creative creation of the new in order to survive and thrive. In the survival process emergence will carry the living system to a more sophisticated level.

The type of complexity needed to create emergence might follow Hegel's doctrine of thesis, antithesis, and synthesis. Hegel believed that all finite things are contradictory and unstable. It is the interaction of the contradictory nature of finite things, Hegel believed, that creates an instability that drives the agitated movement of the entire finite and manifest universe. "Only insofar as something has contradiction in itself does it move, have impulse, or activity, " he wrote.[8] Anything finite by itself is incomplete, Hegel argued, so opposing forces had to be added to the mix until synthesis, or "sublation," was achieved. The emergence of this new condition subsumes and supersedes the original condition.[9]

The emergence of new ideas out of opposing forces was successfully used by President Franklin Delano Roosevelt during the Great Depression to find solutions to the nation's economic ills. He called it "constructive rivalry" and would:

> Use one anonymous informant's information to challenge and check another's, putting both on their toes; he recruited strong personalities and structured their work so that clashes would be certain...In foreign affairs, he gave Moley and Welles tasks that overlapped those of Secretary of State Hull; in conservation and power, he gave Ickes and Wallace identical missions; in welfare, confusing both functions and initials, he assigned PWA to Ickes, WPA to Hopkins; in politics, Farley found himself competing with other political advisors for control over patronage. The effect: the timely advertisement of arguments, with both the experts and the President pressured to consider the main choices as they came boiling up from below.[10]

Roosevelt brought together people with various ideas, perspectives, and agendas and let it all "stew" together. From there new ideas emerged and were implemented, and the country found a way out of its economic dark age.

The opposite case is what the U. S. military refers to as "incestuous amplification," which it defines as "a condition in warfare where one only listens to those who are already in lock-step agreement, reinforcing set beliefs and creating a situation ripe for miscalculation."[11] Some might argue that the rationale for the recent U. S. military excursion into Iraq was predicated on incestuous amplification.

Although incestuous amplification is applied here to a military setting, it has more general applications. When a group gets together with no room for dissent or opposing ideas, it is the defined idea, already set in stone, which inevitably prevails. There is no allowance for the emergence of new ideas; everything is predetermined. The group is of like mind. Everyone sees things in the same light, and anyone who does not is suspect. If Roosevelt had conducted his affairs in this manner, who knows how long it would have taken to come through the Great Depression. Roosevelt's approach was one of complexity that allowed for emergence; incestuous amplification is a linear and deterministic approach that is incapable of spawning creative and emergent solutions.

EMERGENCE AND THE INNATE HEALING FORCE

In terms of health a person with a chronic illness is an example of someone facing a major decision. If the person continues with biomedicine's deterministic approach, in which every illness is seen to have a specific cause, and there is only one specific treatment strategy for that cause, that person's health may deteriorate since biomedicine's track record with chronic illness tends to be poor. The person may choose instead to take another road that attempts to facilitate the emergence of the innate healing force. To do so, as is the case with all instances of emergence, takes a complex, multifaceted, approach.

Instead of seeing the illness as having one specific cause, or having a master planner in the body causing the illness, it is seen as a complex adaptive interaction between person, mind, and environment that is the result of many variables. This way the cause of illness can now be seen as manyfold with many physical, social, emotional, energetic, and/or spiritual aspects to the problem. Instead of seeing illness as having a singular cause with a singular treatment, it is seen as having many causes and needing a treatment strategy that is multifaceted and complex.

For a person with chronic illness the ability to heal might entail a complex approach that is multitiered, multidimensional, and multimodal and helps create the emergence of a new synthesis that allows the person to tap into their innate healing force. In this case the synthesis would lead to the creative emergence of health by using the mechanism of the innate healing force.

The use of multitiered and multimodal approaches to health is not new. Chinese herbal medicine, with a history that dates back over two millennia, uses such a system in the creation of Chinese herbal formulas, which are generally a blend of 4-20 herbs combined in such a way to maximize the synergy and complex nature of the herbs.[12]

David Spiegel, a professor at the Stanford University School of Medicine, conducted support groups for over a decade for women with breast cancer. Along the way he began a study to determine if social support had health benefits. He found something that surprised him: the women with breast cancer in the support group lived an average of 18 months longer than did women with comparable breast cancer and medical care who did not go to such groups.[13]

Dean Ornish of the University of California, San Francisco Medical School conducted a study with patients who had severe coronary heart disease. He placed them in groups and led them through several significant lifestyle changes: a low-fat diet, weekly support groups, stress management classes, classes in yoga and meditation, and an exercise program. He was able to document that after one year in the group for a large percentage of the patients, there was actual reversal of severe atherosclerosis, something that had never previously been accomplished without the use of medication. The success of Ornish's program cannot be attributed to any single, isolated part of the program, even though each component of the program had been shown to be helpful with reversal of heart disease.[14]

Another physician who has been using multimodal approaches is James A. Arond-Thomas of the Center for Complementary Medicine in Ann Arbor, Michigan. Arond-Thomas, who treats a large number of cancer patients, has designed a multimodal treatment strategy for them, based on his belief that healing "encompasses spiritual, mental, emotional, energetic, and physical changes in the multidomain inhibition mechanism." He believes that healing "requires focused attention on (1) disclosing old wounds and hurts, thus allowing the healing light of awareness in; (2) unblocking the flow of emotional energy, allowing this flow to invigorate both the mind and the body; and (3) restoring the normative flow of the innate healing vital energy within each person."[15]

Arond-Thomas' treatment strategy for a woman with breast cancer might include chemotherapy, a nontoxic biologic response modifier, psychoanalysis, relaxation and breath work, guided visualization and meditation, nutritional and herbal supplements, and a guided self-change program. At the heart of his treatment strategy are loving relationships, whether with people in the patient's life, their cellular relationships with the diseased breast, or with themselves.[16]

Arond-Thomas calls his approach "autonomic re-education," or "autonomic autopoiesis," which he believes resets the "inhibition mechanism that provides regulatory controls over the expressive capacity of DNA."[17] By providing controls, autonomic re-education can promote homeostasis and health by bringing about regular cell death. This can lead to self-organization, or autopoiesis, according to Aaron Antonovsky, a pioneer in the biopsychosocial movement, who says, "Once a stable strength has come into being, the human system is capable of a reorganization of self on a higher level of complexity, more capable of pro-action."[18] In other words, people can cultivate the emergence of the new, which can encourage the innate healing force to help a person self-heal. Perhaps this explains how Norman Cousins, who wrote about his experience in *Anatomy of an Illness*, was able to heal himself from his life-threatening ailment of ankylosing spondylitis with the help of laughter, creativity, Vitamin C, and rest.[19] Cousins used his approach to encourage and stimulate the emergence of his innate healing system.

Arond-Thomas thinks that his work is on the cutting edge of new discoveries about "our subliminal depths" and that there is a great profundity of human potential into which each person can tap. He sees that capacity as an important adjunct to his work with patients with chronic illness.[20]

EMERGENCE AND HUMAN POTENTIAL

George Leonard and Michael Murphy, two of the pioneers of the human potential movement, also have created a multifaceted approach, what they call "Integral Transformative Practices." Murphy and Leonard are interested not just in the potential health benefits of such an approach, but also in the potential for positive transformation.[21]

For over 30 years Murphy has studied the field of human potential with an eye on the question: Are the limits of human growth—physical, mental, and spiritual—fixed? As a corollary to that question, he asked, "Are there specific practices through which ordinary people can develop their abilities?" To answer these questions, Murphy wrote a textbook, *The Future of the Body*,[22] in which he presented compelling evidence of the human capacity for metanormal perception, cognition, movement, vitality, and spiritual development. Furthermore, Murphy suggested in his book that the activities that tap into these capacities can be identified and assembled into a coherent program of transformative practice. Such practice, Murphy believes, would constitute a crucial next step in the world's evolutionary direction.

After finishing and publishing his textbook, Murphy and his friend George Leonard began to offer their Integral Transformative Practices program to the general public. In the book they co-authored, *The Life We Are Given: A Long-Term Program for Realizing the Potential of Body, Mind, Heart, and Soul*,[23] they outlined their program and discussed the outcomes they were able to measure through quantitative analysis. Using a series of classroom techniques and home assignments that included physical exercise, meditation and focused attention, affirmations and guided imagery, energy movements, intellectual explorations, and group processing, Murphy and Leonard taught their program to an initial group of 33 for one year on a weekly basis. During the second year they worked with a group of 30 that they again taught on a weekly basis.

Because Murphy and Leonard were interested in knowing if their approach was valid and had measurable benefits, a statistician was hired to analyze results. Some very positive changes were found, especially in the second year group. As Leonard said in an interview with Russell DiCarlo, "The amount of change is really quite spectacular. All sorts of wonderful changes in their body, some of which would have to be called metanormal and extraordinary."[24]

Participants were rated on a scale of zero to ten and the findings were published in the appendix of their book.[25] They found participants achieved an 8.2 (on a zero to ten scale) overall improvement in health, leading Leonard to say in the DiCarlo interview:

> Taking a look at all this gave us some ideas for some very practical applications. We cannot solve our health crisis in a financially viable way. It is impossible to do it no matter what method we use, as long as we continue to use our present method of medical technology, which is sickness based and relies upon expensive drugs and expensive technology. The only way we can make it work is through a radical change in lifestyle. And if we can

change the lifestyle of a group of ordinary Americans, improving their health by 8.2 on a scale of 0 to 10, we can save hundreds of billions of dollars in this country.[26]

Towards a New Renaissance

All of these programs we have discussed show the effectiveness of a multimodal approach. Even without any awareness of complexity or emergence, or how they relate to the innate healing force, multimodal programs are effective. If this is the case, a Quantum-Integral approach, which specifically attempts to use the emergent properties of mind and spirit to trigger the innate healing force, can have profound results.

From an integral perspective, to be effective a multimodal approach needs to be aperspectival and encompass all the aspects that make a person whole—the physical, energetic, social, emotional, cognitive-intellectual, and spiritual. It also needs to have a developmental approach that correlates all the above aspects that make a person whole with an understanding of the evolution of human consciousness. To do this, it must guide people through the prerational, rational, and transrational domains.

To raise people to higher levels of health, thinking and being, a Quantum-Integral Medicine needs to use a multimodal approach that stimulates creative intelligence and quantum thinking capacities. This can help achieve creative transformations in consciousness that open vision to new horizons and potentials. These new potentials are the higher reaches of the mental domain and the spiritual domain that is emerging. Manifestations of these potentials include the triggering of the innate healing force, greater mental capacity, an increase in metanormal capabilities, and greater use of human potential. In other words, it would bring forth the flowering of a new Renaissance, the likes of which has never been seen before.

Chapter Notes

1. Manaka, Yoshio. *Chasing the Dragon's Tail*. Brookline, MA: Paradigm Publications, 1995: 19.

2. Johnson, Steven. *Emergence: The Connected Lives of Ants, Brains, Cities, and Software*. New York: Scribner, 2001: 31.

3. Kauffman, Stuart. *Investigations*. New York: Oxford University Press, 2000.

4. Maturana, Humberto, and Varela, Francisco. *Autopoiesis and Cognition*. London:Reidel, 1980.

5. Capra, Fritjof. *The Hidden Connections*. New York: Doubleday, 2002: 36.

6. de Chardin, Pierre Teilhard. *The Phenomenon of Man*. New York: Harper and Row, 1959.

7. Morowitz, Harold J. *The Emergence of Everything*. New York: Oxford University Press, 2002: 177.

8. Hegel, quoted in Wilber, Ken. *Sex, Ecology, Spirituality*. Boston: Shambhala Publications, 1995: 528.

9. Rohmann, Chris. *A World of Ideas*. New York: Ballantine Books, 1999: 171.

10. Wilensky, quoted in Gladwell, Malcolm. "Connecting the dots." *The New Yorker*. (March 10, 2003): 87.

11. Krugman, Paul. "Delusions of Power." *The New York Times Online*, March 28, 2003: 2. www.nytimes.com/2003/03/28/opinion/28KRUG. html?pagewanted=print&position=top.

12. Bensky, Dan and Randall Barolet. *Chinese Herbal Medicine Formulas and Strategies*. Seattle: Eastland Press, 1990.

13. Spiegel, David. "Social Support: How Friends, Family, and Groups Can Help." In Daniel Goleman and Joel Gurin. *Mind/Body Medicine*. Yonkers, NY: Consumer Reports Books, 1993: 331.

14. Goleman and Gurin, in Goleman and Gurin, *Mind/Body Medicine*, pp. 9-10.

15. Arond-Thomas, James A. "Disclosure and autonomic autopoiesis: A research and treatment model for twenty-first century medicine." *Advances in Mind-Body Medicine*. 16, no. 2 (Spring 2000): 140.

16. Ibid, p. 138.

17. Ibid, p. 140.

18. Antonovsky, Aaron. "A sociological critique of the 'well-being' movement." *Advances: The Journal of Mind-Body Health*. 10, no. 3 (Summer 1994): 7.

19. Cousins, Norman. *Anatomy of an Illness as Perceived by the Patient*. New York: W. W. Norton, 1979.

20. Arond-Thomas, "Disclosure and autonomic autopoiesis: A research and treatment model for twenty-first century medicine," p. 143.

21. Leonard, George and Michael Murphy. *The Life We Are Given: A Long-Term Program for Realizing the Potential of Body, Mind, Heart, and Soul.* New York:Jeremy P. Tarcher/Putnam, 1995.

22. Murphy, Michael. *The Future of the Body: Explorations Into the Further Evolution of Human Nature.* New York: Jeremy P. Tarcher/Putnam, 1992.

23. Leonard and Murphy, *The Life We Are Given: A Long-Term Program for Realizing the Potential of Body, Mind, Heart, and Soul.*

24. Leonard, George. "Human Potential: From Esalen to Mainstreet." Interview by Russell E. DiCarlo. *HealthWorld Online*, 1996: 6. www.healthy.net/asp/templates/interview.asp?id=293&headertitle=conversations+.

25. Leonard and Murphy, *The Life We Are Given: A Long-Term Program for Realizing the Potential of Body, Mind, Heart, and Soul*, pp. 207-13.

26. Leonard, "Human Potential: From Esalen to Mainstreet," p. 7.

Thirteen

The Further Reaches of Healing and Human Potential

I f it is possible for greater mental and spiritual capacities to emerge, then a result of that will be access to levels of healing and human potential that heretofore have only been experienced by a few. If humanity works towards a greater evolutionary emergence of human potential, the examples seen throughout history will only steadily increase in the years to come.

EXTRAORDINARY HUMAN CAPABILITIES

Modern day physicists think that the unification of the four forces of nature can create extraordinary potential. "We could change the structure of space and time, tie our own knots in nothingness, and build matter to order," writes physicist Paul Davies. "Controlling the superforce would enable us to construct and transmute particles at will, thus generating exotic forms of matter. We might even be able to manipulate the dimensionality of space itself."[1]

As the writer and scientist Arthur C. Clarke has written, "Highly advanced technology is essentially indistinguishable from magic. Fortunately, such magic appears to be waiting in the wings of our deepening understanding of the quantum vacuum in which we live."[2]

Scientists are not the only ones who have dared to dream such thoughts. These have been the musings of people since the beginning of man's place on earth. The ancient Chinese text, The Yellow Emperor's Classic of Internal Medicine, which dates back several thousand years, is the original source book of Chinese medicine. It is a dialogue between the Yellow Emperor and his physician, Qi Bo, on the nature of life, the cosmos, heaven, earth, and man's place between heaven and earth. In one chapter, when the Yellow Emperor inquires of Qi Bo about people he heard of from ancient times who knew the secrets of the universe, Qi Bo replies, "Not too long ago there were people known as achieved beings who had true virtue, understood the way of life, and were able to adapt to and harmonize with the universe and seasons…these achieved beings did not live like ordinary humans, who tended to abuse themselves. They were able to travel freely to different times and places since they were not governed by conventional views of time and space."[3]

Religion also has had its share of extraordinary feats. In the New Testament, it is recorded that Jesus performed at least 35 miracles, such as walking on water, healing the sick, multiplying the loaves and fishes, turning water into wine, and raising the dead.[4]

In order to convince his followers of his spiritual powers, it was said that the Buddha put on demonstrations where he would rise into the air, emit flames and streams of water from his body, and walk in the sky. He would also cut his body into pieces, let his head and limbs fall to the ground, and then join them all together again.[5]

Saint Teresa of Avila claimed that she physically levitated during her raptures. Ten separate depositions were taken by nuns who claimed to have watched her rise off the ground.[6] The patron saint of rocketry, Saint Joseph of Cupertino, was said to have levitated on 200 separate occasions. Pope Benedict the Fourteenth, the pope who presided over his canonization proceedings, said, "I sat there and watched all these prominent judges, businessmen—men I trusted—who swore before the Congregation of Rites that Saint Joseph had risen off the ground to quite noticeable heights…I watched this parade of witnesses, and I finally had to believe them."[7]

The modern day spiritual teacher Sri Chimnoy once created 16,000 paintings in a single twenty-four hour period, according to one of his students, who claimed to have counted them.[8] He has also written over 1300 books and has weight lifted over 7000 pounds. Additionally, he plays over 100 musical instruments, all self-taught. Sri Chimnoy has made the transcendence of human limitations his own spiritual practice.[9] Yan Xin, a contemporary doctor of qi gong medicine in China, claims, "Early-stage cancer is curable as easily as the common cold. If the patient works with me, I can reduce mid-stage cancer and control the spread of some late-stage cancer."[10]

SIDDHIS

All these types of extraordinary capacities are known in Hinduism and Buddhism as siddhis and in Catholicism as charisms. They are special attributes that generally arise as byproducts of transformative practice, although they can also arise by themselves spontaneously, and include mystical cognitions, clairvoyance, extraordinary physical abilities, and extraordinary healing abilities.

Eastern traditions actually warn against siddhis, feeling that although they can be a byproduct of transformative practices, by treating them as special they divert energy from seeking one's true nature and cause one to become trapped by the lure of the ego. Eastern traditions also believe that the ability to demonstrate special powers is not a manifestation of one's true nature, nor evidence of enlightenment. As Elmer Green, the founder of biofeedback, said, "A lot of people have confused the siddhis—the powers to control body, emotions, and mind—with spirituality. But the siddhis can be an ego trap...A saint is a person who does what he says."[11]

Although the Buddha demonstrated siddhis to his followers, he also understood they were not the culmination of a cultivated spiritual life. Once by the bank of a river he met a disciple who told him that after 25 years of practicing an ascetic lifestyle, he was capable of crossing the river by walking on the water. The Buddha told him he would have saved himself a lot of time and effort by taking the ferry across, since it only cost a penny.[12]

INTEGRAL TRANSFORMATION

Nonetheless, siddhis can be an outgrowth of integral transformation, or integral enlightenment. Every spiritual tradition recognizes there can be an emanation of light either from the body or from a part of the body of an enlightened person.[13] This phenomenon is seen as an inherent latency, something that can be developed. From an integral perspective, the more aspects of a person that are developed, the more chance there will be for a flowering of a person's attributes, allowing the light that emanates to grow stronger. The light reflects an ability to have greater human potential and to manifest siddhis.

Sri Aurobindo, who developed what he called Integral Yoga and was a proponent of the cultivation of these higher human potentials, wrote:

> We need not shun the siddhis and cannot shun them. There is a stage reached by the yogin when, unless he avoids all action in the world, he can no more avoid the use of the siddhis of power and knowledge than an ordinary man can avoid eating and breathing; for these things are the natural action of the consciousness to which he is rising, just as mental activity and physical motion are the natural action of man's ordinary life. All the ancient rishis used these powers, all great avatars and yogins have used them, nor is there any great man...who does not use them continually in imperfect form, without knowing clearly what are these supreme faculties that he is enjoying.[14]

From an evolutionary standpoint and from the perspective of emergence, extraordinary capabilities are a sign of what might lie ahead and of faculties to come that are manifestations of the emergence of higher levels of mind and spirit. Many spiritual traditions caution followers to turn away from the body because it is a trap set by the ego to hinder transcendence. One mystic wrote, "The body is a dung heap."[15] However, from an integral perspective, the body is a manifestation of the greater spiritual nature, and far from being a dung heap it is a treasure to behold. The emergence of greater levels of mind, and of spirit will allow the development of special capacities in body, mind, and spirit. Quantum-Integral Medicine is an example of a practice that can help to further this emergence along.

EVERYDAY HUMAN POTENTIALS

Although the development of extraordinary human capabilities is one aspect of the emergence of spirit, it is important that everyday human potentials also be cultivated. These are the capacity to live a more full and self-actualized life, to heal more capably and more naturally, to love more readily, to be less caught up in deterministic thinking, to think at a higher and more sophisticated level, and to think more creatively and with more vision. To achieve these, a different type of human potential is needed, one that uses the greater potentials of the mind. From an integral perspective, these characteristics are important aspects of a person's makeup. What good is it to have tremendous metanormal ability if a person's everyday potentials are not being developed?

From a Quantum-Integral perspective, the manifestation of special capacities and the development of the everyday potentials are all components of what Hinduism and Buddhism call *buddhi*, which is considered the enlightened will, awakened mind, and discerning intelligence. Buddhi is a mind that has an innate comprehension of the unity of all things. Buddhi is used to plan or dream or imagine what can be done.

> It makes formations for the future which the will can try to carry out if opportunity and circumstances become favorable or even it can work to make them favorable. In men of action this faculty is prominent and a leader of their nature; great men of action always have it in a very high measure. But even if one is not a man of action or practical realization or if circumstances are not favorable or one can do only small and ordinary things, this vital mind is there. It acts in them on a small scale, or if it needs some sense of largeness, what it does very often is to plan in the void, knowing that it cannot realize its plans or else to imagine big things, stories, adventures, great doings in which oneself is the hero or the creator…It concerns itself with a pursuit of pure truth and right knowledge; it seeks to discover the real Truth behind life and things and our apparent selves and subject its will to the law of Truth.[16]

To awaken buddhi is to realize a more integrated mode of existence. With the advent of buddhi, higher levels of mind can emerge, allowing a person to quantum think, think at a higher level, think more creatively and with more vision. Buddhi may be the highest ideal for which one can strive.

Emergence and Higher Levels of Existence

The developmental perspective of Spiral Dynamics mapped eight stages of existence (see pages 121-125). The first six are considered first tier, and the next two are considered second tier. Research has shown that most people exist at the mid to upper first tier levels; very few exist at the second tier levels where the higher levels of mind, or buddhi, would be. Beyond the second tier would lie the third tier, where spiritual illumination and the manifestation of siddhis would lie. Obviously, if very few people exist at the second tier levels, only a tiny fraction would be in or on their way to the third tier. This tier is so small that Spiral Dynamics does not elaborate on it.

Historically, large-scale leaps to new levels of existence occur when a critical mass reaches a specific level of existence. If things continue in this way, there may be a greater movement towards higher levels of existence in the coming years. Ken Wilber has speculated that society is on the cusp of a dramatic change in consciousness and that within the next decade there will be a large shift in thinking, with eight percent of the population progressing to the second tier.[17]

If a significant number find their way to second tier in the coming years, there may be a greater witnessing of the emergence of the higher levels of mind. It may be that as more people progress to the second tier, a certain percentage will progress to the third tier. If that occurs, there may then occur a greater witnessing of the emergence of spirit. However, to attain these higher levels people cannot just sit and wait for something to happen. A certain amount of work has to be done to encourage emergence.

It was the German poet, playwright, philosopher, and scientist Goethe (1749-1832) who said, "If you want to advance into the infinite, explore the finite in all directions." From a Quantum-Integral Medicine perspective the way to explore the finite in all directions is for people to explore and exercise the various aspects of their being—the physical, energetic, social, emotional, cognitive-intellectual, and spiritual. The more they do this, the more opportunity they will have to advance toward the infinite and encourage the emergence of their higher human potentials. These higher potentials will facilitate healing and encourage the greater use of human potential, whether it is the capability to manifest extraordinary human capacities, or to live a fuller and more human life.

Every person is capable of rising to higher levels of existence and by so doing, realizing higher aspects of their potential and broadening the scope of their vision. It will not be just their personal vision that will be expanded, but it will be a larger vision that will look at society and the world and consider what types of creative solutions can be formulated to help heal the ailments of a world in disarray.

This is the approach of Quantum-Integral Medicine. Using quantum thinking, it will encourage/nurture the emergence of higher levels of existence and in the process help establish a healthy vision, one that attempts to awaken buddhi in self, culture, and society and in the process help heals self, culture, and society.

The Medicine of the Future

It was Thomas Edison who said that "the doctor of the future will give no medicine." What kind of system of medicine would this be, if this were the case? It would be one in which the healer would understand that the mind and body of the patient are capable of summoning vast inner resources to meet the challenge at hand. It would also be one in which, as Norman Cousins wrote, "The most valuable service a physician can provide to a patient is helping him to maximize his or her own recuperative and healing potentialities."[18]

Perhaps there will never be a day when drugs are not used. But if we get to the point where we fully encourage the innate healing system's abilities, there could be a considerable lessening on the reliance of them. One of the greatest healers of the twentieth century, the Nobel laureate Albert Schweitzer (1875-1965), who was not only a physician but also a theologian, philosopher, and musicologist, said "Each patient carries his own doctor inside him. They come to us not knowing that truth. We are at our best when we give the doctor who resides within each patient a chance to go to work."[19]

The medicine of the future could be practiced in hospitals and private and public clinics. Health providers of various modalities, in partnership, could conceivably work side by side in these settings, also in partnership with the patient. To get to this point will take a major shift in the way medicine is practiced. But it can be done. The system is starting to change, partly by demand and partly by necessity.

Chapter Notes

1. Davies, Paul. *Superforce: The Search for a Grand Unified Theory of Nature.* New York: Simon and Schuster, 1984: 168.

2. Clarke, quoted in Schwartz, Gary E.R. and Linda G.S. Russek. *The Living Energy Universe*. Charlottesville, VA: Hampton Roads Publishing Co., 1999: 134.

3. Ni, Maoshing. *The Yellow Emperor's Classic of Internal Medicine*. Boston: Shambhala Publications, 1995: 4.

4. Morrow, Lance. "How to Believe in Miracles." *Time*. 138, no. 26 (Dec. 30, 1991):68.

5. Ibid, p. 69.

6. Murphy, Michael. *Transforming the Human Body*. Interview by Jeffrey Mishlove. Thinking Allowed Productions, 1998: 6. www.intuition.org/txt/murphy.htm.

7. Ibid, p. 7.

8. Furman, Ashrita. " 'I am not the body; I am the soul.' Breaking limits with Sri Chimnoy and Ashrita Furman." Interview by Elizabeth Debold. *What is Enlightenment?* No. 22 (Fall/Winter 2002): 68.

9. Ibid, p. 66.

10. Xin, quoted in Dong, Paul and Thomas E. Rafill. *China's Super Psychics*. New York: Marlowe & Company, 1997: 105.

11. Green, in Schwartz, Tony. *What Really Matters: Searching for Wisdom in America*. New York: Bantam, 1995: 137.

12. Morrow, "How to Believe in Miracles," p. 69.

13. Murphy, Michael. "Integrating the Big Bang." Interview by Andrew Cohen. *What is Enlightenment?* No. 15 (Spring/Summer 1999): 90.

14. Aurobindo, Sri. *The Collected Works, Vol. 27, Sapta-Chatusthaya. Pondicherry*, India: Sri Aurobindo Ashram, 1976: 366.

15. A Kempis, quoted in Murphy, Michael. *The Future of the Body: Explorations Into the Further Evolution of Human Nature*. New York: Jeremy P. Tarcher/Putnam, 1992: 172.

16. Aurobindo, in Dalal, A.S. *A Greater Psychology: An Introduction to the Psychological Thought of Sri Aurobindo*. New York: Tarcher/Putnam, 2001: 47, 51.

17. Wilber, Ken. *Speaking of Everything*. Audio interview on CD produced by www.enlightenment.com, 2001.

18. Cousins, Norman. *Anatomy of an Illness as Perceived by the Patient*. New York: W. W. Norton, 1979: 184.

19. Schweitzer, quoted in Cousins, *Anatomy of an Illness as Perceived by the Patient,* p. 87.

Epilogue

I believe that with the proper tools people can be encouraged to use more of their innate healing and human potential capabilities. Most people need to be educated in learning how to expand their thinking and in the process expand their mental models. Science has shown that the universe is larger and more open-ended than most people are led to believe. While this knowledge has major ramifications in the various walks of life, most science ignores it and continues to operate in the well tread path of scientism and reductionism, in the process making its calculations in a linear and deterministic way. Unfortunately, most people follow this lead and think in the same deterministic way.

I believe the facts are there to support the concept of an open-ended universe capable of self-organizing to new levels of emergence. The challenge is to help people to grasp this concept and accept and embrace it, and by so doing motivate them to expand their worldviews.

I have developed a training and certification program to help people do just that. You can learn more about it by going to the website www.quantumintegralcenter.com.

Glossary

Age of Enlightenment: the period in Europe during the seventeenth and eighteenth centuries, when a new age enlightened by reason, science, and a respect for humanity was thought to be emerging. Perhaps the strongest attribute of this time was an abiding faith in the power of human reason.

Aperspectival: a term developed by Swiss philosopher Jean Gebser, signifying a way of thought free of exclusive and limiting perspectives. It is a pluralistic, multiple-perspectives view.

Aperspectival Madness: the belief that no belief is any better than any other.

Autonomic Autopoiesis: a medical model that uses a multimodal approach to promote homeostasis and health by resetting the inhibition mechanism over the expressive capacity of DNA.

Autopoiesis: a network pattern in which the network is produced by its components, and in turn the network produces its components. Also known as self-making.

Biomedicine: Western or modern medicine. Biomedicine tends to view humans as the sum total of their biological processes.

Biopsychosocial Medicine: a model that takes into account the person's biological, psychological, social, and cultural relationships.

Buddhi: a term from Hinduism and Buddhism meaning the enlightened will, awakened mind, and discerning intelligence.

Butterfly Effect: from chaos theory. The technical term is sensitive dependence on initial conditions. The Butterfly Effect refers to the concept that if a butterfly flaps its wings on one continent, it could within a short time period affect the weather in another part of the world.

Chaos Theory: has shown that instead of a universe that runs on clockwork laws, ours is a universe prone to complex and unpredictable outcomes. Since the middle of the twentieth century it has become an accepted science.

Chinese Medicine: a system of medicine, begun in China, that dates back thousands of years and is composed of different modalities, the best known of which is acupuncture. Chinese herbal medicine is another modality. The core concept in Chinese medicine is that the body has an energy circuit, known as qi, or chi, that underlies the body's physiological structures.

Chronic Illness: an ailment that has affected the body for a duration of time, generally six months or more, and will recur frequently. Chronic illness is generally much more difficult to cure than acute illness, since it affects the body in a number of different ways, often concurrently. Usually it is predicated on a breakdown of the body's immune system.

Clockwork Universe: the universe was conceived by Newton and his contemporaries as being similar to a clock that runs with precision and mechanical efficiency. In fact, the popular image of the day was that of a universe that ran with the mechanical efficiency of a clock.

Cognition: the act or process of knowing.

Collapse of the Wavefunction: the transition from quantum reality and the world of many possibilities into the world of one reality; the transition itself is the collapse of the wavefunction.

Complementary Medicine: an umbrella term for alternative medicine, which is considered to complement western medicine.

Complex Adaptive System: a living system that acquires information about its environment and then adjusts itself into a new model in accordance with the information received.

Complexity: in twentieth century science it is order at the edge of chaos.

Complexity Theory: the study of complexity in various systems.

Consciousness: the state of being aware of mind; something within oneself that creates cognition.

Constructive Rivalry: the creation of an emergence of new ideas by allowing opposing forces and ideas to meld in a dynamic way.

Creative Thinking: the ability to think differently, outside the norm of critical thinking, with it emphasis on linear thinking.

Developmentalism: a model of life that is based on the premise that there is an evolutionary direction to the universe and that humans go through certain stages of development as part of this evolutionary direction.

Diversity: one of nature's fundamental laws that there is tremendous variation and diversity in life from single-celled creatures to viruses, plant life, invertebrates, vertebrates, and humans. The time-honored view of biology is that of unity within diversity.

Dogmatic Thinking: thinking characterized by rigidity and a failure to examine sufficiently the premises for the thinking. Often the person holds an opinion in an assertive and authoritative manner, without adequate grounds for doing so.

Edge of Chaos: the boundary between order and chaos, where systems display the greatest complexity.

Emergence: the creation of new life or new properties in response to variables.

Entelechy: the development of a living system's full potential by the actualization of its native potential.

Euclidean Geometry - branch of mathematics that is concerned with such problems as determining the areas and diameters of two-dimensional figures and the surface areas and volumes of solids.

Evidence-Based Medicine: a biomedical model that advocates that biomedicine rely solely on efficacies established through randomized double blind studies, as opposed to clinical experience.

Evolution: the process of change from simple life forms to more complex life forms.

First Tier: terminology in the Spiral Dynamics model of developmentalism that connotes the first six levels of existence.

Frontier Medicine: a field of study within the National Center for Complementary and Alternative Medicine, defined as complementary and alternative medicine practices for which there is no plausible biomedical explanation.

Frontier Science: science that is outside the mainstream, but has a significant number of researchers within its domain asking questions. Topics that fall within its purview include consciousness studies and the science underlying alternative medicine.

Great Chain of Being: an ancient Greek belief, predicated on the idea that reality has a purpose that is informed by spirit.

Human Potential: the intrinsic wellspring of potential that humans have, of which very little is utilized.

Hyperspace: a multidimensional model of space, in which there are many extra and possibly an infinite number of dimensions beyond the standard four of space-time.

Incestuous Amplification: a military term signifying a situation in which people in decision-making positions only listen to those who agree with their perspective.

Infinity: unlimited in time, space, or quantity; boundlessness.

Innate Healing System: the system within the body that is the catalyst for self-healing.

Integral Theory: an approach that attempts to look at life from the broadest perspective possible and then find the unifying thread amongst all fields and all truths.

Integral Transformative Practices: a multifaceted, multidimensional approach to health and transformation.

Integrative Medicine: a medical model that attempts to be inclusive of various modalities from different medical systems and use them together in a coherent and integrated manner.

Kosmos: from the ancient Greeks, meaning the patterned whole of all existence, a matrix that includes the physical, emotional, mental, and spiritual realms.

Laws of Thermodynamics: a component of classical physics, it is the theory of heat and statistical mechanics. The first law of thermodynamics deals with the conservation of energy, the second law with entropy. Currently, it is understood that these laws only apply to closed systems, whereas in open systems chaos and complexity theories are more relevant.

Liar's Paradox: a mind puzzle devised by ancient Greek philosophers and logicians that had no easy way out.

Linear Determinism: based on a world in which everything can be explained causally, it has primarily been applied to physical laws, leading to the belief that this is a clockwork universe driven by an endless sequence of cause and effect.

Logic: the search for truth using a method that contains valid and consistent reasoning, as opposed to illogic, which uses invalid, inconsistent reasoning.

Logos: defined by the ancient Greeks as the power that brings the world into order; they viewed this power as the active creative principle.

Luminiferous Ether: a hypothetical jelly-like substance that was believed to be the vehicle that light used to travel throughout the universe.

Many Worlds: the theory from quantum physics that postulates that if an event has every possibility until the collapse of the wavefunction occurs, then all these possibilities are occurring simultaneously in many worlds throughout the universe.

Mental Models: deeply held images of how the world works, which impact the way people perceive the world and how they think.

Metaphysical Foundations of Modern Science: assumptions that underpin modern scientific theories regarding how the world operates. Neither articulated nor brought into question during research, they can not be proven by empirical experiments.

Michelson-Morley Experiment: an experiment by two physicists meant to prove the existence of the luminiferous ether. Instead, it did the opposite, proving there was no luminiferous ether.

Mind-Body Medicine: a system of medicine that believes the mind and body interact, allowing the mind to play a role in illness and health.

Multimodal Approaches: a medical model that advocates the use of a number of different approaches and modalities for healing purposes.

Non-Euclidean Geometry: a branch of geometry developed in the nineteenth century by a number of mathematicians, including the German mathematician Bernard Riemann. Riemann showed that a geometry in which no parallel lines occurred was equally possible and that the three-dimensional shape of the universe was bent in four-dimensional space into the shape of a hypersphere.

Nonlinear Dynamics: the study of nonlinear systems, which are found in a wide variety of natural, social, and economic systems.

Nonlocal Medicine: the capacity for mind to be a factor in healing, both within and between persons, thus laying the groundwork for the possibility of distance healing.

Nonlocality: action at a distance, amongst quantum objects without apparent causation. The action can occur across great distances, and the interaction can travel at speeds faster than the speed of light.

Noosphere: the collective mental activity of humans; the domain of the mind.

Nous: the world mind, or universal intelligence.

Paradigm: an ideal or example that provides a model to be emulated. Also, as put forth by Thomas Kuhn, an accepted theory that reflects and upholds certain established viewpoints. These are generally adhered to for the sake of keeping these viewpoints dominant.

Participatory Universe: the understanding that the universe is an enormous feedback loop and that the universe and the observer exist as a pair.

Perspectival: using reason to create perspective. First seen in the Renaissance era when artists and scientists started to use perspective to explore the three-dimensionality of space.

Photoelectric Effect: suggests that light is composed of particles called photons, whose energy is proportional to the frequency of the light radiation.

Physical Medicine: the way of medicine as practiced by biomedicine. Its basic tenet is that all illness has a physical basis, and all therapy focuses solely on the physical alteration of the body via drugs and surgery. The brain is a factor in physical medicine, but mind and consciousness are not.

Placebo Effect: improvement in the condition of a person with an illness, without the use of a specific treatment.

Principle of Complementarity: a principle postulated by Niels Bohr and developed in response to the understanding that an electron is both a wave and a particle. Bohr maintained that the particle and wave were complementary, and both were needed to fully understand the nature of an electron.

Psychophysics: the interaction of mind and consciousness with nature.

Quantum Leap: an abrupt movement from one area to another done in a discontinuous manner in which there is no smooth transition from one space to the next.

Quantum Stone Age: the period of time between 1900 and 1925 in which physicists were discovering a new model to explain the laws of the universe, but did not yet have one coherent theory that could give it a solid scientific foundation.

Quantum Theory: the section of physics, developed by a number of physicists in the early part of the twentieth century, that deals mainly with the subatomic realm. Its findings have given the world a new model of physical reality.

Quantum Thinking: a way of thinking that has as its parallel the discontinuous, nonlinear way in which quantum leaps are made. Creative thinking and quantum thinking are closely tied together.

Quantum Vacuum: a vacuum composed of an infinite amount of information and energy that is pervasive throughout the universe. Thought to be the source of the Big Bang and the birthplace of the universe, also believed to be the origin of matter.

Reductionism: the act of reducing complex things or phenomena down to the simplest component or simplest terms, leading to an oversimplification.

Remembered Wellness: a term coined by noted mind-body medicine pioneer Herbert Benson to explain the mechanism of the placebo effect.

Remote Viewing: viewing not limited by space and time.

Renaissance - a "rebirth," that was a series of literary and cultural movements in the fourteenth, fifteenth, and sixteenth centuries, begun in Italy and eventually expanded into Germany, France, England, and other parts of Europe.

Rock Logic: thinking that believes there is only one right, absolute answer.

Santiago Theory of Cognition: theory developed by cognitive scientists Humberto Maturana and Francisco Varela that states that the process of knowing is directly identified with the process of life.

Science: knowledge that is gathered in a systematic manner into general truths.

Scientific Materialism: scientific theories of natural laws that explain things solely in terms of objective processes, thereby creating a scientific model in which the entire universe is explained by and reduced to physical laws.

Scientism: belief that the entire world can be fully explained in the language of objective processes.

Second Tier: terminology in the Spiral Dynamics model of developmentalism that connotes the seventh and eighth levels of existence.

Self-Actualization: the process whereby human beings use their innate instinct to grow and achieve their potential.

Self-Healing: the utilization of the body's innate healing system to heal from chronic and degenerative illness.

Self-Organization: the innate sense of order that living systems have that keeps them always organizing towards order.

Siddhis: special attributes that usually arise out of transformative practices that lead to a greater enhancement of human potential and human possibility. These attributes include mystical cognitions, clairvoyance, extraordinary physical abilities, and extraordinary healing abilities.

Spiral Dynamics: developmental model originally postulated by the late professor of psychology, Clare Graves. It postulates that there are eight general levels of existence.

Spirit: something immaterial that is believed by spiritual traditions to give life to all physical organisms and non-physical entities.

Spiritual: relating to spirit and sacred matters and to an individual's sense of being connected to a greater whole.

Spontaneous Remission: a term used by biomedicine as an attempt to explain how people with serious chronic and degenerative ailments experience profound healing. In the biomedicine view there is no logical causative factor, hence, the belief that it is a spontaneous healing.

Supermind: a very evolved and powerful level of consciousness; a realm of cosmic consciousness and spiritual illumination.

Synchronization: in living systems, it is a unity and harmony among components of the system that leads it towards creation of a greater whole.

Systems Theory: a correlative of complexity theory that seeks to find the underlying commonality of a system. In the process, it views living systems as integrated wholes that cannot be reduced to smaller parts.

Teleology: ancient Greek belief that the universe had a greater purpose.

Theory of Everything: the all-embracing physics theory of the universe that hopes to unite the four forces of nature. Scientists in some other fields believe that to be all-embracing, a theory of everything needs to encompass psychophysics, the interaction of mind and consciousness on nature.

Third Tier: using terminology from the Spiral Dynamics model of developmentalism, third tier connotes levels of existence beyond the first eight levels of existence. Because very few people exist at the third tier level, Spiral Dynamics does not elaborate on it. Nonetheless, it is an authentic level of existence.

Transrational: a level of thinking and existence that adheres to rational thinking, but at the same time understands the limits of rational thinking and at appropriate times will use a more intuitive way of thinking.

Triggering Mechanism: a hypothesized mechanism in the body that switches on the innate healing system when it is triggered.

Turbulence: something that causes a disturbance; an instability that transforms order into disorder and predictability into unpredictability.

Uncertainty Principle: a theory devised by Werner Heisenberg that states that if a particle's location is known, the momentum can't be known; and if the momentum is known, the location can't be known.

Virus: a causative agent of disease that can range from a simple microorganism to an extremely complex set of molecules that can invade a cell and manipulate the host's replication machinery, causing the cell to replicate more viruses.

Water Logic: the opposite of rock logic. The user of this type of logic is more prone to flexible thinking, creating an environment conducive to creative thinking.

Worldview: a way of seeing the world that is mentally ingrained.

Zen Buddhism: a system of philosophy that is an offshoot of Buddhism. It was first introduced into Japan in the twelfth century.

Bibliography

Adams, PF, GE Hendershot and MA Marano. "Current estimates from the National Health Interview Survey." *Vital Health Statistics*. 10 (1999): 1996.

Angier, Natalie. "How biology affects behavior and vice versa." *The New York Times*.(May 30, 1995): C1, C7.

Antonovsky, Aaron. "A sociological critique of the 'well-being' movement." Advances: *The Journal of Mind-Body Health*. 10, no. 3 (Summer 1994): 6-12.

Argyris, Chris. *Reasoning, Learning, and Action: Individual and Organizational.* San Francisco: Josey-Bass, 1982.

Arond-Thomas, James A. "Disclosure and autonomic autopoiesis: A research and treatment model for twenty-first century medicine." *Advances in Mind-Body Medicine*. 16, no. 2 (Spring 2000): 135-48.

Astin, John. "Why patients use alternative medicine." *Journal of the American Medical Association*. 279, no. 19 (1998): 1548-53.

Aurobindo, Sri. *Essays on the Gita*. New York: E.P. Dutton and Co, 1950.

Aurobindo, Sri. *The Collected Works, Vol. 27, Sapta-Chatusthaya*. Pondicherry, India: Sri Aurobindo Ashram, 1976.

Aurobindo, Sri. *The Life Divine*. Pondicherry, India: Sri Aurobindo Ashram Trust, 1990.

Barasch, Marc. "A psychology of the miraculous." *Psychology Today*. 27, no. 2 (March/April 1994): 54-60.

Barraclough, Kevin. "Medical heroes." *British Medical Journal*. 326, no. 7380 (Jan. 11, 2003): 111-13.

Beck, Don. "The never-ending upward quest: The practical and spiritual wisdom of spiral dynamics." Interview by Jessica Roemischer. *What is Enlightenment? No. 22* (Fall/Winter 2002): 105-26.

Beck, Don and Chris Cowan. *Spiral Dynamics: Mastering Values, Leadership, and Change*. Malden, MA: Blackwell Publishers, 1996.

Bensky, Dan and Randall Barolet. *Chinese Herbal Medicine Formulas and Strategies*. Seattle: Eastland Press, 1990.

Benson, Herbert and Richard Friedman. "Harnessing the power of the placebo effect and renaming it remembered wellness." *Annual Review of Medicine*. 47 (1996): 193-99.

Bloch, Sidney. "Moses Maimonides' contribution to the biopsychosocial approach in clinical medicine." *Lancet*. 358, no. 9284 (Sept. 8, 2001): 829-32.

Bohr, Niels. *Atomic Physics and Human Knowledge*. New York: Wiley, 1958.

Borges, Jorge Luis. "Avatars of the Tortoise." In *Labyrinths*. New York: New Directions, 1962, 202-08.

Bower, Bruce. "Getting into Einstein's brain." *Science News*. 127 (May 25, 1985): 330-31.

Boyd, William. *The Spontaneous Regression of Cancer*. New York: Charles C. Thomas, 1996.

Braud, William and Rosemarie Anderson. *Transpersonal Research Methods for the Social Sciences*. Thousand Oaks, CA: Sage Publications, 1998.

Brown, Walter. "The placebo effect." *Scientific American*. 278, no. 1 (Jan. 1998): 90-95.

Buzan, Tony and Barry Buzan. *The Mind Map Book*. New York: Plume, 1996.

Byrd, Randolph C. "Positive therapeutic effects of intercessory prayer in a coronary care unit population." *Alternative Therapies in Health and Medicine*. 3, no. 6 (Nov. 1997): pp. 87-90.

Cantor, Georg. *Gesammelte Abhandlugen*. Edited and translated by A. Fraenkel and E. Zermelo. Berlin: Springer-Verlag, 1932.

Capra, Fritjof. *The Hidden Connections*. New York: Doubleday, 2002.

Capra, Fritjof. *The Tao of Physics*. Berkeley: Shambhala Publications, 1975.

Capra, Fritjof. *The Turning Point*. New York: Bantam, 1982.

Capra, Fritjof. *The Web of Life*. New York: Anchor Books, 1996.

Casti, John L. and Werner DePauli. *Godel: A Life of Logic*. Cambridge, MA: Perseus Publishing, 2000.

Chalmers, David. "The puzzle of conscious experience." *Scientific American*. 273, no. 6 (June 1995): 78-82.

Chan, Wing-Tsit. *A Source Book in Chinese Philosophy*. Princeton: Princeton University Press, 1963.

Chang, Raylene and Richard C. Page. "Characteristics of the self-actualized person: Visions from the east and west." *Counseling and Values*. 36, no. 1 (Oct. 1991): 2-10.

Clark, Jane. Foreword in Jane Clark and Willis Harman (eds.). *New Metaphysical Foundations of Modern Science*. Sausalito, CA: Institute of Noetic Sciences, 1994, ix-xiii.

Cleary, Thomas. *Rational Zen: The Mind of Dogen Zenji*. Boston: Shambhala Publications, 1992.

Cleary, Thomas. *Zen Essence: The Science of Freedom*. Boston: Shambhala Publications, 1989.

Cleese, John. "Basil Fawlty, manager." *Newsweek*. 133, no. 7 (Feb. 15, 1999): 47.

Cousins, Norman. *Anatomy of an Illness as Perceived by the Patient*. New York: W. W. Norton, 1979.

Cousins, Norman. "Healer Within." In *The Parabola Book of Healing*. New York: Continuum Publishing, 1994, 125-27.

Cousins, Norman. "Tapping human potential." *Second Opinion*. 14, no. 1 (July, 1990): 55-70.

Csikszentamihalyi, Mihalyi. *Creativity: Flow and the Psychology of Discovery*. New York: HarperCollins, 1996.

Csikszentmihalyi, Mihaly, and Robert Epstein. "A creative dialogue." *Psychology Today*. 32, no. 4 (July/August 1999): 58-61.

Dalai Lama. *Mindscience*. Boston: Wisdom Publications, 1991.

Dalal, A.S. *A Greater Psychology: An Introduction to the Psychological Thought of Sri Aurobindo*. New York: Tarcher/Putnam, 2000.

Davies, Paul. *Superforce: The Search for a Grand Unified Theory of Nature*. New York: Simon and Schuster, 1984.

Davies, Paul and John Gribbin. *The Matter Myth*. New York: Simon and Schuster, 1992.

De Bono, Edward. *I Am Right, You Are Wrong*. New York: Penguin Putnam, 1990.

De Broglie, Louis. *Matter and Light*. New York: Dover, 1946.

de Chardin, Pierre Teilhard. *The Phenomenon of Man*. New York: Harper and Row, 1959.

De Laplace, Pierre-Simon. *Philosophical Essays on Probabilities*. Translated by Andrew I. Dale. New York: Springer-Verlag, 1995.

Dixey, Richard. "Man, matter and metaphysics: Can we create a total science?" In Jane Clark and Willis Harman (eds.). *New Metaphysical Foundations of Modern Science*. Sausalito, CA: Institute of Noetic Sciences, 1994, 133-56.

Dong, Paul and Thomas E. Rafill. *China's Super Psychics*. New York: Marlowe & Company, 1997.

Dossey, Larry. "Antonovsky's perspective may not go far enough." *Advances: The Journal of Mind-Body Health*. 10, no. 3 (Summer 1994): 13-15.

Dossey, Larry. "Canceled funerals: A look at miracle cures." *Alternative Therapies in Health and Medicine*. 4, no. 2 (March 1998): 10-1 8, 116-20.

Dossey, Larry. *Healing Words: The Power of Prayer and The Practice of Medicine*. San Francisco: HarperSanFrancisco, 1993.

Dossey, Larry. *Recovering the Soul: A Scientific and Spiritual Search*. New York: Bantam, 1989.

Dossey, Larry. *Reinventing Medicine*. New York: HarperCollins Publishers, 1999.

Dossey, Larry. "The forces of healing: Reflections on energy, consciousness, and the beef stroganoff principle." *Alternative Therapies in Health and Medicine*. 3, no. 5 (Sept. 1997): 8-14.

Dove, Rick. "Enterprise Mandelbrots and self-organization." *Automotive Production*. 108, no. 10 (Oct. 1996): 16-17.

"EBM: Unmasking the Ugly Truth." *British Medical Journal*. 325, no. 7378 (Dec. 21, 2002): 1496-98.

Eddington, Arthur Stanley. *New Pathways in Science*. New York: Macmillan, 1935.

Eddington, Arthur. *The Nature of the Physical World*. New York: Macmillan, 1929.

Edmundson, Mark. "The teacher who opened my mind." *Utne Reader*. 115 (Jan.-Feb. 2003): 74-79.

Ehin, Charles. "The ultimate advantage of self-organizing systems." *Journal for Quality and Participation*. 18, no. 5 (Sept. 1995): 30-38.

Eisenberg, David et al. "Trends in alternative medicine use in the United States, 1990 1997." *Journal of the American Medical Association*. 280, no. 18 (1998): 1569-75.

Engel, George L. "The need for a new medical model: The challenge for biomedicine." *Science*. 196, no. 4286 (April 8, 1977): 129-36.

Falconar, Ted. *Creative Intelligence and Self-Liberation*. Bancyfelin, Carmarthen, Wales: Crown House Publishing, 2000.

Fee, Elizabeth and Theodore M. Brown. "Alice Hamilton: Settlement physician, occupational health pioneer." *American Journal of Public Health*. 91, no. 11 (Nov. 2001): 1767-1769.

Feynman, Richard. *The Character of Physical Law*. Cambridge, MA: MIT Press, 1965.

Firestien, Roger. *A Workshop on Consciousness and Creativity*. Held in Saratoga Springs, NY, March 30, 2001.

Fisher, Anne. "Afternoon movies and other keys to creativity." *Fortune*. 140, no. 6 (Sept. 27, 1999): 240-44.

Fisher, Arthur. "The cosmic connection." *Popular Science*. 238, no. 4 (1991): 70-77.

Flowers, Charles. *A Science Odyssey: One Hundred Years of Discovery*. New York: William Morrow, 1998.

Folger, Tim. "Does the universe exist if we're not looking?" *Discover*. 23, no. 6 (June 2002): pp. 44-49.

Folger, Tim. "Quantum shmantum." *Discover*. 22, no. 9 (Sept. 2001): 36-43.

Furman, Ashrita. " 'I am not the body; I am the soul.' Breaking limits with Sri Chimnoy and Ashrita Furman." Interview by Elizabeth Debold. *What is Enlightenment?* No. 22 (Fall/Winter 2002): 66-77.

Galilei, Galileo. *Two New Sciences*. Translated by Henry Crew and Alfonso De Salvio. New York: Macmillan, 1914.

Gebser, Jean. *The Ever-Present Origin*. Translated by Noel Barstad and Algis Mickunas. Athens, Ohio: Ohio University Press, 1985.

Gell-Mann, Murray. *The Quark and the Jaguar*. New York: W.H. Freeman and Company, 1994.

Gladwell, Malcolm. "Connecting the dots." *The New Yorker*. (March 10, 2003): 83-88.

Glanz, James. "Physicist ponders God, truth, and a 'final theory.'" *The New York Times Online*. www.nytimes.com/library/national/science/012500sci-scientist-weinberg.htm. (25 Jan. 2000).

Glanz, James. "Reconciling nothingness in the universe and the soul." *The New York Times Online*. www.nytimes.com/library/national/science/120799sci-essay-nothingness.htm. (7 Dec. 1999).

Gleick, James. *Chaos: Making a New Science*. New York: Penguin Books, 1987.

Glenn, Jim. *Scientific Genius: The Twenty Greatest Minds*. Avenel, NJ: Crescent Books, 1996.

Goldberger, Ary L., David R. Rigney and Bruce J.West. "Chaos and fractals in human physiology." *Scientific American*. (Feb. 1990): 43-49.

Goleman, Daniel and Joel Gurin. "What is Mind/Body Medicine?" In Daniel Goleman and Joel Gurin. *Mind/Body Medicine*. Yonkers, NY: Consumer Reports Books, 1993, 3-18.

Gonzales, R, DC Malone, JH Maselli and MA Sande. "Excessive antibiotic use for acute respiratory infections in the United States." *Clinical Infectious Diseases*. 33, (2001): 757-62.

Goodwin, Brian C. "Toward A Science of Qualities." In Jane Clark and Willis Harman (eds.). New Metaphysical Foundations of Modern Science. Sausalito, CA: *Institute of Noetic Sciences*, 1994, 215-50.

Goodwin, James S. "Chaos and the limits of modern medicine." *Journal of the American Medical Association*. (Nov. 5, 1997): 1399-1400.

Goswami, Amit. *Quantum Creativity: Waking Up to Our Creative Potential*. Cresskill, NJ: Hampton Press, 1999.

Goswami, Amit. *The Self-Aware Universe: How Consciousness Creates the Material World*. New York: Jeremy P. Tarcher/Putnam, 1993.

Greene, Brian. *The Elegant Universe*. New York: W. W. Norton & Company, 1999.

Gribbin, John. *In Search of Schroedinger's Cat*. New York: Bantam, 1984.

Grim, Pamela. "Too close to Ebola." *Discover*. 24, no. 6 (June 2003): 43-47.

Hadamard, Jacques. A*n Essay on the Psychology of Invention in the Mathematical Field*. Princeton: Princeton University Press, 1945.

Hall, Stephen S. "Cheating fate." *Health Magazine*. 6, no. 2 (April 1992): 38-45.

Hameroff, Stuart and Roger Penrose. "Orchestrated objective reduction of quantum coherence in brain microtubules: The orch OR model for consciousness." In Stuart Hameroff, W. Kaszniak and A.C. Scott (eds.). *Toward a Science of Consciousness: The First Tucson Conference Discussion and Debates*. Cambridge, MA: MIT Press, 1996.

Hamilton, Craig. "Why Sri Aurobindo is cool." *What is Enlightenment?* No. 21 (Spring/Summer 2002): 66-77, 152-61.

Haraway, Donna Jeanne. *Crystals, Fabrics, and Fields: Metaphors of Organicism in Twentieth-Century Developmental Biology.* New Haven: Yale University Press, 1976.

Harman, Willis. "Toward a Science of Wholeness." In Jane Clark and Willis Harman (eds.). *New Metaphysical Foundations of Modern Science.* Sausalito, CA: Institute of Noetic Sciences, 1994, 375-95.

Harris, Paul L. "The last of the magicians? Children, scientists, and the invocation of hidden causal powers." *Child Development.* 68, no. 6 (Dec. 1997): 1018-20.

Hawking, Stephen. "A brief history of relativity." *Time.* 154, no. 27 (Dec. 31, 1999): pp. 67-81.

Hawking, Stephen. *A Brief History of Time.* New York: Bantam, 1988.

Hawking, Stephen. *Black Holes and Baby Universes.* New York: Bantam, 1993.

Hawking, Stephen. *The Universe in a Nutshell.* New York: Bantam, 2001.

Heikkinen, Terho and Asko Jarvinen. "The common cold." *Lancet.* 361, no. 9351 (Jan. 4, 2003): 51-59.

Heisenberg, Werner. *Physics and Philosophy.* London: Faber, 1959.

Henry, J. "Magic and science in the sixteenth and seventeenth centuries." In R.C. Olby, G.N. Cantor, J.R.R. Christie and M.J.S. Hodge (eds.). *Companion to the History of Science.* London: Routledge, 1990.

Herbert, AP. "The common cold." *In Look Back and Laugh.* London: Methuen, 1960, 115-17.

Herbert, Nick. Consciousness and Quantum Reality. Interview by Jeffrey Mishlove. *Thinking Allowed Productions.* www.intuition.org/txt/herbert.htm. (1998).

Herbert, Nick. *Quantum Reality.* New York: Anchor Books, 1985.

Hewitt, Bill and Tom Duffy. "In faith and hope." *People.* 50, no. 23 (Dec. 21, 1998): 146-48.

Hirshberg, Caryle and Marc Barasch. *Remarkable Recovery.* New York: Riverhead Books, 1995.

Ho, Mae-Wan. "Toward an Indigenous Western Science: Causality in the Universe of Coherent Space-Time Structures." In Jane Clark and Willis Harman (eds.). *New Metaphysical Foundations of Modern Science*. Sausalito, CA: Institute of Noetic Sciences, 1994, 179-213.

Hochgesang, Jennifer. "An end to painful periods." *Natural Health*. (July-August, 1998): 76-80.

Hofstadter, Douglas R. *Godel, Escher, Bach: An Eternal Golden Braid*. New York: Vintage Books, 1979.

Horrigan, Bonnie. "Papa Henry Auwae Po'okela la'au lapa'au: Master of Hawaiian medicine." *Alternative Therapies in Health and Medicine*. 6, no. 1 (Jan. 2000): pp. 83-88.

Jahn, Robert and Brenda Dunne. "The Spiritual Substance of Science." In Jane Clark and Willis Harman (eds.). *New Metaphysical Foundations of Modern Science*. Sausalito, CA: Institute of Noetic Sciences, 1994: 157-77.

Jaspers, Karl. *The Great Philosophers*. New York: Harcourt Brace and Co, 1981.

Jeans, James. *The Mysterious Universe*. Cambridge: Cambridge University Press, 1931.

Johnson, Steven. *Emergence: The Connected Lives of Ants, Brains, Cities, and Software*. New York: Scribner, 2001.

Jueneman, Frederic B. "Hyperspace." *R & D*. 37, no. 11 (August 1995): 54-58.

Kabat-Zinn, Jon. "Indra's net at work: The mainstreaming of dharma practice in society." In G.Watson, S. Batchelor and G. Claxton (eds.). *The Psychology of Awaking: Buddhism, Science, and Our Day-to-Day Lives*. London: Rider, 1999, 225-49.

Kaku, Michio. *Hyperspace*. New York: Oxford University Press, 1994.

Kamolz, T and V. Velanovich. "Psychological and emotional aspects of gastroesophageal reflux disease." *Diseases of the Esophagus: The Official Journal of the International Society for Diseases of the Esophagus*. 15, no. 3 (2002): 199-203.

Kauffman, Stuart. *Investigations*. New York: Oxford University Press, 2000.

Kegan, Robert. "Epistemology, fourth order consciousness, and the subject-object relationship or...How the self evolves." Interview by Elizabeth Debold. *What is Enlightenment?* No. 22 (Fall/Winter 2002): pp. 143-54.

Keynes, John Maynard. *Essays in Biography.* London: Macmillan, 1951.

Kimura, Yasuhiko. "A philosopher of change." An interview by Carter Phipps. *What is Enlightenment?* No. 22 (Fall/Winter 2002): 22-35.

Koestler, Arthur. *The Roots of Coincidence.* London: Hutchinson, 1972.

Kothari, D. S. "Complementarity principle and syadvada." In A.P. French and J.P. Kennedy (eds.). *Niels Bohr.* Cambridge, MA: Harvard University Press, 1985.

Koyre, Alexandre. *From the Closed World to the Infinite Universe.* Baltimore: John Hopkins University Press, 1957.

Krugman, Paul. "Delusions of Power." *The New York Times Online.* www.nytimes.com/2003/03/28/opinion/28krug.html?pagewanted =print&position=top. (28 March 2003).

Kuhn, Thomas. *The Structure of Scientific Revolutions.* Chicago: University of Chicago Press, 1962.

Leonard, George. *Education and Ecstasy.* Berkeley: North Atlantic Books, 1968.

Leonard, George. "Human Potential: From Esalen to Mainstreet." Interview by Russell E. DiCarlo. *HealthWorld Online,* www.healthy. net/asp/templates/interview.asp?id=293&headertitle=conversati ons+. (1996).

Leonard, George. *The Silent Pulse.* New York: E.P. Dutton, 1978.

Leonard, George. Transforming Human Nature. Interview by Jeffrey Mishlove. *Thinking Allowed Productions,* www.intuition.org/txt/ smith.htm. (1998).

Leonard, George and Michael Murphy. *The Life We Are Given: A Long-Term Program for Realizing the Potential of Body, Mind, Heart, and Soul.* New York: Jeremy P. Tarcher/Putnam, 1995.

LeShan, Lawrence. *The Medium, the Mystic, and the Physicist.* New York: Ballantine Books, 1974.

Levenstein, Susan. "Wellness, health, Antonovsky." *Advances: The Journal of Mind-Body Health.* 10, no. 3 (Summer 1994): 26-29.

Lewit, K. "Changes in locomotor function, complementary medicine, and the general practitioner." *Journal of the Royal Society of Medicine.* 139, no. 12 (1994): 36-39.

Lindley, David. *Where Does the Weirdness Go?* New York: BasicBooks, 1996.

Littlejohn, GO and J. Walker. "A realistic approach to managing patients with fibromyalgia." *Current Rheumatology Reports.* 4, no. 4 (August 2002): 286-92.

Lovejoy, Arthur. *The Great Chain of Being.* Cambridge, MA: Harvard University Press, 1936.

Lovelock, James. *Gaia.* New York: Oxford University Press, 1987.

Lown, Bernard. *The Lost Art of Healing.* New York: Houghton Mifflin, 1996.

Madigan, Marsha. "Consciousness: A principle-based paradigm for leadership." *Business Spirit Journal Online.* www.bizspirit.com/bsj/current/feal.html. (Dec. 1999).

Maimonides, Moses. *The Medical Aphorisms of Moses Maimonides.* New York, Yeshiva University Press, 1970.

Manaka, Yoshio. *Chasing the Dragon's Tail.* Brookline, MA: Paradigm Publications, 1995.

Maslow, Abraham. *The Farther Reaches of Human Nature.* New York: Penguin Books, 1971.

Maslow, Abraham. *Toward A Psychology of Being.* New York: Van Nostrand Reinhold, 1968.

Matthews, Robert. "Nothing like a vacuum." *New Scientist.* 145, no. 1966 (Feb. 25, 1995): 30-33.

Maturana, Humberto, and Varela, Francisco. *Autopoiesis and Cognition.* London: Reidel, 1980.

Merchant, Carolyn. *The Death of Nature*. New York: Harper & Row, 1980.

Michalko, Michael. *Cracking Creativity*. Berkeley: Ten Speed Press, 2001.

Michalko, Michael. *Thinkertoys*. Berkeley: Ten Speed Press, 1992.

Mitchell, Edgar. *A Workshop on Consciousness and Creativity*. Held in Saratoga Springs, NY, March 30, 2001.

Morowitz, Harold J. *The Emergence of Everything*. New York: Oxford University Press, 2002.

Morrow, Lance. "How to Believe in Miracles." *Time*. 138, no. 26 (Dec. 30, 1991) 68-69.

Murphy, Michael. Transforming the Human Body. Interview by Jeffrey Mishlove. *Thinking Allowed Productions*. www.intuition.org/txt/murphy.htm. (1998).

Murphy, Michael. "Integrating the Big Bang." Interview by Andrew Cohen. *What is Enlightenment?* No. 15 (Spring/Summer 1999): pp. 82-96, 156-59.

Murphy, Michael. *The Future of the Body: Explorations Into the Further Evolution of Human Nature*. New York: Jeremy P. Tarcher/Putnam, 1992.

Nadeau, Robert, and Menas Kafatos. *The Non-Local Universe*. New York: Oxford University Press, 1999.

"Names and FA." *The Boston Globe* (Nov. 1, 1980).

National Center for Complementary and Alternative Medicine. www.nccam.com.

Needham, Joseph. *Science in Traditional China*. Cambridge, MA: Harvard University Press, 1981.

Newton, Isaac. *Sir Isaac Newton's Mathematical Principle of Natural Philosophy and His System of the World*. Translated by A. Motte and Florian Cajori. Berkeley: University of California Press, 1962.

Ni, Maoshing. *The Yellow Emperor's Classic of Internal Medicine*. Boston: Shambhala Publications, 1995.

Nielson, WR and R. Weir. "Biopsychosocial approaches to the treatment of pain." *Clinical Journal of Pain*. 17, no. 4 Supplement (Dec. 2001): S114-27.

Noble, Ivan. "Centuries-old puzzle solved." *BBC News Online*. news. bbc.co.uk/low/english/sci/tech/newsid_1820000/1820643.stm. (Feb. 20, 2002).

O'Regan, Brendan and Caryle Hirshberg. *Spontaneous Remission: An Annotated Bibliography*. Sausalito, CA: Institute of Noetic Sciences, 1993.

Ortner, Jon. *Where Every Breath is a Prayer*. New York: Stewart, Tabori, and Chang, 1996.

Osborn, Alex F. (1953). *Applied Imagination: Principles and Procedures of Creative Problem-Solving*. New York: Charles Scribner and Sons.

Ostriker, Alicia (ed.). *William Blake: The Complete Poems*. New York: Penguin, 1977.

Patterson, C. H. *The Therapeutic Relationship: Foundations for an Eclectic Psychotherapy*. Belmont, CA: Brooks/Cole, 1985.

Pear, Robert. "Investigators find repeated deception in ads for drugs." *The New York Times Online*. Query.www.nytimes.com/search/ restricted/artile?res=F00C1FF83C5F0c778CDDAB0994DA4. (4 Dec. 2002).

Planck, Max. *Where is Science Going?* New York: Norton, 1932.

Radin, Dean. *The Conscious Universe*. San Francisco: HarperSanFrancisco, 1997.

Redfield, James, Michael Murphy and Sylvia Timbers. *God and the Evolving Universe*. New York: Jeremy P. Tarcher, 2002.

Remen, Rachel Naomi. *Kitchen Table Wisdom: Stories That Heal*. New York: Riverhead Books, 1996.

Ringel, Y and DA Drossman. "Irritable bowel syndrome: Classification and conceptualization." *Journal of Clinical Gastroenterology*. 35, no. 1 Supplement (July, 2002): S7-S10.

Rohmann, Chris. *A World of Ideas*. New York: Ballantine Books, 1999.

Root-Bernstein, Robert and Michele Root-Bernstein. *Sparks of Genius*. New York: Houghton Mifflin, 1999.

Rubik, Beverly. "Exploring the Frontiers of Science." Interview by Russell DiCarlo. *HealthWorld Online*. www.healthy.net/asp/templates/interview.asp?PageType=Interview&ID=297. (1996).

Rubik, Beverly. *Frontier Science*. Interview by Daniel Redwood, www.drredwood.com/interviews/rubik.html. (1999).

Rucker, Rudy. *Infinity and the Mind*. Princeton: Princeton University Press, 1995.

Sackett, DL, WS Richardson, W Rosenberg and RB Haynes. *Evidence-Based Medicine: How to Practice and Teach*. London: Churchill-Livingstone, 1997.

Saher, P.J. *Eastern Wisdom and Western Thought: A Comparative Study in the Modern Philosophy of Religion*. London: George Allen and Unwin, Ltd., 1969.

Scheinin, Richard. "Dalai Lama explores ties that bind science and religion." *Tribune News Service*. (April 25, 1994)

Schlitz, Marilyn. "Researcher Profile: Francisco J. Varela." *Institute of Noetic Sciences Archives*, www.noetic.org/ions/publications/review_ archives/frontiers_of_re.../frontiers_46_42.htm. (1998).

Schoofs, Mark. "Healing head trips." *The Village Voice*. 43, no. 19 (May 12, 1998): 22.

Schroedinger, Erwin. *Nature and the Greeks*. Cambridge: Cambridge University Press, 1954.

Schroedinger, Erwin. *Science, Theory, and Man*. New York: Dover, 1957.

Schwab, E.D. and K.J. Pienta. "Cancer as a complex adaptive system." *Medical Hypotheses*. 47, 3 (Sept. 1996): 235-41.

Schwartz, Gary E.R. and Linda G.S. Russek. *The Living Energy Universe*. Charlottesville, VA: Hampton Roads Publishing Co., 1999.

Schwartz, Tony. *What Really Matters: Searching for Wisdom in America*. New York: Bantam, 1995.

Senge, Peter. *The Fifth Discipline*. New York: Bantam Doubleday Dell, 1990.

Shealy, C. Norman. *Sacred Healing*. Boston: Element Books, 1999.

Sicher, Fred, Elisabeth Targ, Dan Moore and Helene S.Smith. "A randomized double-blind study of the effect of distant healing in a population with advanced AIDS." *Western Journal of Medicine*. 169, no. 6 (Dec. 1998): 356-63.

Sirag, Saul-Paul. Consciousness and Hyperspace. Interview by Jeffrey Mishlove. *Thinking Allowed Productions*, www.intuition.or/txt/sirag. htm. (1998).

Smith, Huston. Beyond the Post-Modern Mind. Interview by Jeffrey Mishlove. *Thinking Allowed Productions*, www.intuition.org/txt/ smith.htm. (1998).

Spiegel, David. "Social Support: How Friends, Family, and Groups Can Help." In Daniel Goleman and Joel Gurin. *Mind/Body Medicine*. Yonkers, NY: Consumer Reports Books, 1993, 331-49.

Srole, L. and AK Fischer. "The Midtown Manhattan longitudinal study versus 'The mental paradise lost' doctrine." *Archives of General Psychiatry*. 37 (1980): 209-21.

Stapp, Henry P. "Quantum physics and the physicist's view of nature: philosophical implications of Bell's theorem." In Richard E. Kitchener (ed.). *The World View of Contemporary Physics*. Albany, NY: S.U.N.Y. Press, 1988.

Stein, Ron. "Tracing the brain's obscure path to perception." *The Washington Post*. (Feb. 22, 1999): D7.

Stone, Elizabeth. "Is there a God? Am I crazy?" *Elle*. 10, no. 4 (Dec. 1994): 60.

Sulmasy, Daniel P. "Is medicine a spiritual practice?" *Academic Medicine*. 74, no. 9 (Sept. 1999): 1002-05.

Suzuki, D. T. *Zen Buddhism*. Garden City, NY: Anchor Books, 1956.

Sweeney, Kieran and David Kernick. "Clinical evaluation: Constructing a new model for post-normal medicine." *Journal of Evaluation in Clinical Practice*. 8, no. 2 (May 2002): 131-38.

Talbot, Margaret. "The placebo prescription." *The New York Times Sunday Magazine Online*. www.nytimes.com/library/magazine/ home/20000109mag-talbot7.html. (9 Jan. 2000).

Tannenbaum, Sandra J. "Evidence and expertise: The challenge of the outcomes movement to medical professionalism." *Academic Medicine*. 74, no. 7 (July 1999): 757- 63.

Targ, Russell and Jane Katra. *Miracles of Mind*. Novato, CA: New World Library, 1998.

Temoshok, Lydia. "We need to study the psychosocial impact of medical interventions." *Advances: The Journal of Mind-Body Health*. 13, no. 1 (Winter 1997): 51-53.

Theodoropoulos, Demetrios S., Farrin A. Manian and James S. Goodwin. "Modern medicine and chaos theory (includes reply)" (Letter to the editor). *Journal of the American Medical Association*. (March 18, 1998): 835-36.

Thomas, Lewis. "Self-regulation through imagery. Part 2: Visualization and cancer therapy." In Norris, P. *Newsletter of the International Society for the Study of Subtle Energies and Energy Medicine*. 3, no. 2 (1992): 2-5.

Towne, Charles. "Gathering of the realms: the convergence of science and religion." *Science and Spirituality*. 10, no. 1 (1999): 18-19.

Trembath, Michael. "Vibrational healing and Samvahan massage." *WellBeing Magazine*. No. 64 (1999): 36-39.

Varela, Francisco, Evan Thompson and Eleanor Rosch. *The Embodied Mind*. Cambridge, MA: MIT Press, 1993.

Villanueva, Pilar, Salvador Peiro, Julian Librero and Inmaculada Pereiro. "Accuracy of pharmaceutical advertisements in medical journals." *Lancet*. 361, no. 9351 (Jan. 4, 2003): 27-32.

Wald, George. "The Cosmology of Life and Mind." In Jane Clark and Willis Harman (eds.). *New Metaphysical Foundations of Modern Science*. Sausalito, CA: Institute of Noetic Sciences, 1994: 123-31.

Wallis, Claudia. "Faith and healing." *Time*. 147, no. 26 (June 24, 1996): 58-63.

Wang, Hao. "What is logic?" *The Monist*. 77, no. 3 (July 1994): 261-77.

Weinstock, Charles. "Type M: Do you have a miracle personality?" *Psychology Today*. 27, no. 2 (March/April, 1994): pp. 61-62.

Wenger, Win and Richard Poe. *The Einstein Factor*. Rocklin, CA: Prima Publishing, 1996.

West, Thomas, G. *In the Mind's Eye: Visual Thinkers, Gifted People with Learning Difficulties, Computer Images, and the Ironies of Creativity*. Buffalo, NY: Prometheus Books, 1991.

Westfall, Robert. *Never at Rest: A Biography of Isaac Newton*. Cambridge, England:Cambridge University Press, 1980.

Wheatley, Margaret J. *Leadership and the New Science*. San Francisco: Berrett-Kohler, 1999.

Wilber, Ken. *A Theory of Everything*. Boston: Shambhala Publications, 2000(a).

Wilber, Ken. "How big is our umbrella." *Noetic Sciences Review Online Archives*, Winter. www.noetic.org/ions/archivelisting_fram. asp?ID=291.(1996).

Wilber, Ken. *Integral Psychology*. Boston: Shambhala Publications, 2000(b).

Wilber, Ken. *Sex, Ecology, Spirituality*. Boston: Shambhala Publications, 1995.

Wilber, Ken. *Speaking of Everything*. Audio interview on CD produced by www.enlightenment.com, 2001

Wilber, Ken. *The Eye of Spirit*. Boston: Shambhala Publications, 1997.

Wilber, Ken. *The Marriage of Sense and Soul*. New York: Random House, 1998.

Wilczek, Frank. "The end of physics?" *Discover*. 14, no. 3 (March 1993): 30-32.

Wilson, Tim and Tim Holt. "Complexity and clinical care." *British Medical Journal*. 323 (Sept. 2001): 685-88.

Winston, Michael R. "Aurobindo Ghose and world reconstruction." *Journal of Religious Thought*. 51, no. 1 (Summer/Fall 1994): 7-23.

Zebrowski, George. "Life in Godel's universe: Maps all the way." *Omni*. 14, no. 7 (April 1992): 53-57.

Zohar, Danah. *Rewiring the Corporate Brain*. San Francisco: Berrett-Koehler, 1997(a).

Zohar, Danah. *The Quantum Self*. New York: Quill/William Morrow, 1990.

Zohar, Danah. *Who's Afraid of Schroedinger's Cat?* New York: Quill/William Morrow, 1997(b).

Zuger, Alan. "New way of doctoring: By the book." *The New York Times*. (Dec. 16, 1997): Sect. B, 11 (col. 3).

Zweig, A. "Gustav Theodor Fechner." In Paul Edwards. *The Encyclopedia of Philosophy, Vol. 3*. New York: Macmillan, 1967, 175-99.

Index

About the Author

Michael Wayne, Ph.D., L.Ac., is a licensed acupuncturist and board certified Chinese herbalist, with over 25 years experience in Chinese medicine. His Ph.D. is in Quantum-Integral Medicine, which is about the science of emerging properties and its relationship to the innate healing system and human potential. Dr. Wayne is the founder and director of the Center for Quantum-Integral Medicine.

Dr. Wayne is also the creator of the IdeaLab, an organization dedicated to using creative intelligence and quantum thinking to develop new and emerging ideas that can be implemented in the fields of medicine, business, technology, and the arts.

In addition, Dr. Wayne teaches a class in Psychoneuroimmunology at Skidmore College in Saratoga Springs, NY.

He resides in upstate NY with his wife and son.

For information on Michael Wayne's classes, seminars, lectures, professional consulting, and the IdeaLab, here is his contact information:

Website: http://www.quantumintegralcenter.com
Email: Michael@quantumintegralcenter.com